MENSA®

PRESENTS

A COMPENDIUM OF CONUNDRUMS

THIS IS A CARLTON BOOK

Text and puzzle content copyright © British Mensa Limited 1998
Design and artwork copyright © Carlton Books Limited 1998

This edition published by Carlton Books Limited 1998

A CIP catalogue for this book is available from the British Library.

ISBN 1-85868-457-9

Printed and bound in Great Britain

MENSA®

PRESENTS

A COMPENDIUM OF CONUNDRUMS

A special collection of some of the best brain–teasers ever written

Peter Jackson

CARLTON

ARE YOU SMART ENOUGH TO JOIN MENSA?

Solving puzzles can be a rewarding experience, and the moment you discover you have unravelled the puzzle compiler's convoluted logic always brings a glow of satisfaction. But we thought you deserved something more, so Mensa are offering tangible proof of your mental prowess. Solve the following fiendishly difficult puzzle and we will send you a free certificate as proof of your achievement:

Two perfectly straight trees grow 50 feet apart. One is 30 feet high and the other 40 feet high. There is a bird of prey at the top of each tree. A vole is feeding at some point on the ground in a direct line with the two trees. Both birds spot the vole at the same time and swoop down together, and each bird covers exactly the same distance. Neither bird has seen the other until the last second, and inevitably they crash together in the air inches from the vole. In the confusion, the vole escapes.

How far from the foot of each tree was the vole feeding?

There, you did it! Write the answers on a postcard, together with your name and address, and send them to Mensa Puzzle Challenge, Mensa House, Freepost, Wolverhampton, WV2 1BR, England (no stamp needed). If your answers are correct, we will send you a certificate and details of how you can apply to become a Mensa member.

If you don't live in Britain and you'd like more details, you can contact:
Mensa International, 15 The Ivories, 628 Northampton Street, London N1 2NY, England
who will be happy to put you in touch with your own national Mensa.

CONTENTS

About Mensa   **4**

Introduction   **7**

The Conundrums   **8**

The Answers   **117**

INTRODUCTION

Welcome to my world of conundrums – a world where the only problems that exist are the ones on the page in front of you, a world where the only pressure to find a solution comes from within yourself. The frustrations are real; the anxieties are real; the sheer mind-bending, stomach-churning, nail-biting, wall-thumping vexations are real, but they are all self-induced. You can stop when you want to. You can come out of this world of puzzles and back to reality whenever you wish, but you will be back.

This is a world where you can escape the mundane routine of everyday life, a competition where the only competitor is yourself. You can cheat if you want to; you can look at the answer as soon as you read the question if you wish, but if you do you will be missing the joy of finding the solution for yourself.

When you have taken the challenge, grasped the nettle, wrestled with it, searched the innermost corners of your mind for inspiration and found it, then the feeling of elation derived from finding the solution will have you addicted.

I have composed the puzzles in such a way as to make each one different from the last, with the exception of the series puzzles, which are the first in the book. Some of them, I admit, require certain mathematical skills, but I have limited the mathematical knowledge required to that expected of a 15- or 16-year-old. The other questions do not require any kind of specialist knowledge at all, but they do require tenacity, logical thinking and endurance.

Now please read on.

IN ORDERED SUCCESSION

One of the easiest forms of puzzles to set, but not to solve, is the series puzzle. You know, the type that asks you to find the missing number from a row of numbers. I know only too well that when new ideas seem to elude the puzzle setter's mind, the temptation to resort to composing yet another series puzzle can be overwhelming.

In order to discipline myself not to write a book full of such conundrums but yet cater for those people who happen to like solving them, I have begun this compendium of mind-teasers with 10 such puzzles. I make no apologies for this, and I cannot promise not to include any more within these pages, but I thought it would be better to get these out of the way before embarking on the more adventurous types of puzzle.

Each term given below is related to its neighbor in some way, no matter how obscure that relationship may seem. You are asked to find the missing term in each case.

1.	1	3	6	11	18	29	?
2.	4	5	9	18	34	59	?
3.	1	2	5	11	21	36	?
4.	2	8	24	64	160	284	?
5.	0.5	0.75	0.8333'	0.875	0.9	0.91666'	?
6.	2	6	18	54	162	486	?
7.	7	?	63	189	?	1701	
8.	2	12	30	56	90	132	?
9.	1	5	15	34	65	111	?
10.	1	3	7	15	31	63	?

see answer page 202

THE FOUR JAYS

Four friends, Jane, June, Jean and Jenny discovered that, if a number was designated to each letter of their names and added together, it produced their ages.

June is 17, Jenny is two years older, while Jane and Jean are both sweet 16. All the girls agree that June is in her prime.

Can you find the numbers the girls assigned to each letter of their names?

see answer page 202

Acutting blade for a woodworking machine, shown in the diagram below, had to be manufactured from a blank piece of steel. He needed to know the radius of the curved section in order to form his grinding wheel to the correct shape. This was not given on his drawing and needed to be calculated. His mathematical abilities were limited, so he asked his boss and his workmates to help, but he could find no one with enough knowledge to assist him. His boss, being an impatient sort of person, insisted that the cutter be made without further delay. In desperation the man tried to make the blade by trial and error. After many attempts, and several grinding wheels later, he was dismissed for not being able to do his job properly.

If you had been there, could you have solved the problem for him?

see answer page 202

THE FARMER'S FIELDS

A farmer owned two pieces of land. The first was eight times larger in area than the other, and the two were separated by an access road. He grazed cattle on the first, while he grew vegetables in the other.

As time went by, it became necessary to replace the fencing that surrounded the two fields. When the farmer measured the perimeters of both sections of land, he was surprised to find that it was going to take twice as much fencing to surround the smaller area than it was to surround the larger.

Both sections of land were rectangular in shape and the fences were continuous. The gates of the fields were to be a removable section of fence.

How much fencing did he need to buy?

see answer page 202

THREE LITTLE BOYS

Three little boys who were comparing their allowance money found that each of them had only one type of coin in his pocket.

The first had his money all in five-cent coins, the second had all ten-cent coins, and the third had only fifty-cent coins.

The boys thought that it would only be fair if they had equal amounts of money. Mental arithmetic was not their strongest subject, so they started exchanging coins, recounting after each exchange.

After some time they eventually ended up with $1.80 each, and found that each boy had given two of his original coins to each of the other two boys.

How many of each type of coin did each of the boys have to begin with?

see answer page 202

A popular form of code is to assign numbers to letters so that a sentence becomes a sequence of seemingly unrelated numbers.

In the next puzzle I have reversed the process and given each number a letter. In this code, however, there is a mathematical relationship between the letters. I could make the puzzle easier by saying what that relationship is, but I'm sure you can solve the puzzle without any help, can't you?

$$\text{CAB} = \text{CGHGF}$$
$$\text{DAB} = \text{HGGGFH}$$
$$\text{GIB} = \text{GB}$$
$$\text{CACH} = \text{GCCD}$$

Can you find which numbers have been assigned to each of the letters?

see answer page 202

THE ENGINEER

An engineer of international reputation was assigned the job of constructing a foundation for the siting of a large piece of machinery. The machine was very heavy and the reinforced concrete foundation, 1 m thick, had to be a high specification both in strength and in flatness. This part of the job was not a problem for the engineer as he had organized such a construction many times before. The problem arose from the way the machine was to be fastened to the foundation.

Due to the high vibrations the machine was subject to when fully working, the normal method of drilling the concrete and fastening the machine to its foundation with anchor bolts after final positioning was not acceptable.

The manufacturers of the machine gave instructions that pockets would be cast into the concrete at specific locations as the foundation was being laid, the idea being that after final positioning a special compound would be poured into the cavities and the holding down bolts dropped into it. The compound would then harden within 24 hours and provide a permanent, vibration-resistant location for the machine.

The pockets were to be in the shape of an inverted 'T'. The cavity had to be 200mm below the surface of the concrete and in the shape of a 150mm cube. A hole of 30mm diameter would connect the cavity to the surface to allow access for the compound and for the bolt.

No wooden or other type of shuttering could be used, as these could not be removed after the concrete had set. Neither could they be left in situ, because they would eventually rot and allow the hardened compound to become loose in the cavities.

The engineer tried long and hard to think of a way of forming the cavities. He thought of using blocks of ice supported from below – he could then cast the concrete and the ice would melt, leaving the necessary pockets. He dismissed the thought almost at once. The ice would freeze the water in the concrete mix and cause it to crumble around the place where strength was most needed.

Eventually he hit on an idea which he put into action immediately. The idea worked, and the foundation was cast to everyone's satisfaction.

How did he do it?

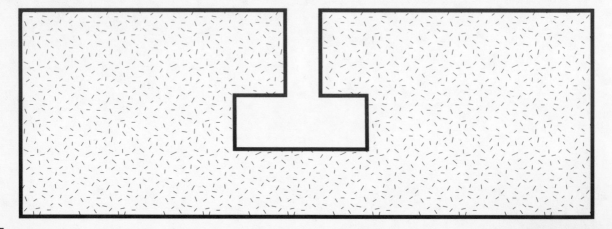

see answer page 202

The goods yard at the railway company's depot was fitted with an oval track and two branch lines. This track was normally used by apprentice engine drivers to gain experience of handling locomotives, but occasionally it was used to store goods before dispatch if all the sidings were occupied. At the far end of the oval track was a narrow tunnel, which was just wide enough to allow the engine to pass through it.

On this occasion two freight carriers, situated at either side of the oval, had been loaded with cargo that was wider than the tracks. A mistake had been made and the wrong cargo had been loaded on to the wrong carriage. The cargo on the first carriage should have been put on to the second carriage and vice versa.

As there was no access road around the track, the simplest solution to the problem seemed to be to move the carriages into their correct locations using a locomotive. The manager of the depot asked one of the apprentices to do this.

'But the loads are too wide to pass through the tunnel,' protested the apprentice as he studied the task.

'That's right,' replied the manager, 'but to someone of your intelligence that shouldn't be a problem. By the way, the engine is on one of the branch lines. I want it back in its place when you've finished.'

So the problem is: move carriage A into the position of carriage B, carriage B into the position of carriage A and put the engine back into the siding. Remember the engine can pass through the tunnel, but the carriages cannot.

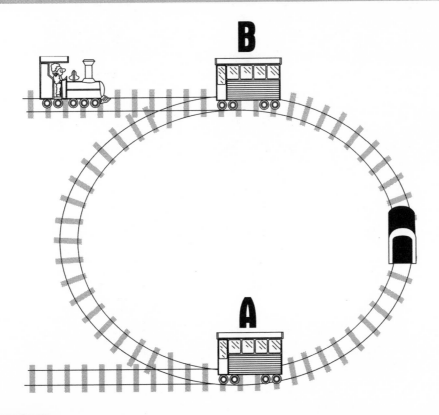

see answer page 203

SERVING THE WINE

The manager of a small restaurant buys his house wine in bulk from the local cash-and-carry. The wine comes in plastic containers of two different sizes. One holds five units and the other holds three.

The wine is included in the price of the meal and the manager allows 1/4 of a unit of wine per person. This is normally served by placing a jug of wine in the center of the table for the customers to help themselves as and when they require it.

On a particular busy evening with a party of 16 people arriving in 10 minutes' time, he finds that he has only one of each size container of wine left in stock. For 16 people, all seated together, two jugs would be required, each holding two units of wine. He has two identical glass jugs, but no method of measuring exactly two units, all other jugs and containers being in use at this time.

As he is a fair-minded business man, the manager refuses to give the customers short measure, but by the same token he will not give them more wine than they have paid for. He devises a way, by using only the jugs and the containers, of serving precisely two units of wine in each jug and leaving exactly two units of wine in each of the containers for future use.

How does he do it?

see answer page 203

teacher at a local school decides to improve the young children's arithmetic by teaching them how to measure. He explains that most things are measurable, and demonstrates with a number of different measuring instruments. He sets the pupils a number of tasks involving measurement, and asks them to calculate such things as area, change in temperature, weight of different objects, etc. For homework he asks them to use measuring instruments that they have in their homes to measure and calculate whatever they choose. The next day, as he is marking the homework, he opens the book belonging to little Tommy Tomkins and is dismayed to see:

$$7 + 10 = 5$$
$$8 + 17 = 1$$
$$4 + 11 = 3$$
$$9 + 7 = 4$$
$$6 + 8 = 2$$
$$5 + 7 = 12$$

Angered by what he sees, he immediately sends for little Tommy. 'This work is a disgrace,' he cries, 'only one right out of six simple additions, you ought to be ashamed.'

'But they are all the right answers,'protests Tommy. 'I checked them carefully, every one of the sums is correct.'

The teacher, his patience a little strained, allows Tommy to explain why he thinks the answers are correct.

After hearing Tommy's explanation the teacher agrees that the sums all have the right answers.

What did Tommy say to the teacher?

see answer page 203

GET IT OUT!

Mechanical engineers are often faced with this type of problem: how to successfully remove a worn bearing from its location without damaging the housing or surrounding parts of the machinery.

There are many different types of bearing extractors or pullers on the market to assist the engineer in most situations. However, there are some situations in which even the most sophisticated of tools are of little help. This occurs when the bearing has been pressed into a blind hole and there is no room to locate any kind of extractor behind the offending part.

One trick of the trade is to heat up the housing, expanding the surrounding metal, thus making the hole larger and allowing the bearing to become free in its location and be removed easily. But there are times when for practical reasons this is not possible.

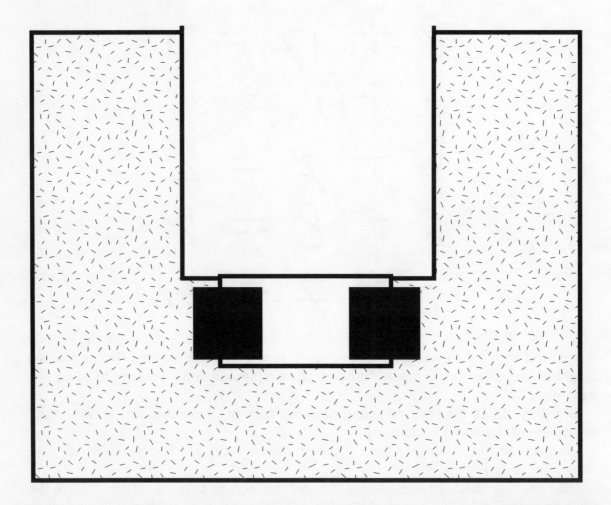

In the diagram above I've shown such a situation. How does the engineer remove the bearing without damage to himself or to the housing, without special tools and without heating up the surrounding metal?

see answer page 204

CHASING THE GIRLS

Alex and Phillip were good friends who lived in a large apartment building. Alex lived at number 60, while Phillip lived at number 102. Alex wanted to become friendly with a girl from the ground floor. He knew she lived at number 12, as he had often seen her entering that apartment on the way home from school. He wanted to know her name but was too shy to ask.

Phillip was infatuated, too, but with a girl who lived on the top floor. Her name was Diana, but she refused to tell him her apartment number, saying something about not wanting him hanging around outside her door.

The boys had known for some time that there was a link between their names and their apartment numbers. They wondered if they could use the same link to discover the name of the girl from number 12 and the number of the apartment where Diana lived. They tried the system and found that it worked.

What was the name of the girl from number 12, and in which apartment did Diana live?

see answer page 204

MORE MPG

Mr Stingy lives at the bottom of a very steep hill. His son and his family live exactly one mile away at the top of the hill. The son does not own a car, and there is no public transport between the two houses. Mr Stingy, much to his displeasure, has to drive to the son's house every week in order to see his grandchildren.

He calculates that because of the steepness of the hill and the constant use of low gears, his car only produces 10 miles to a gallon of fuel on the upward journey. This is compensated for by the fact that on the downward journey, he can almost free-wheel, and the car produces 100 miles to the gallon for that one mile.

Assuming that he uses his car for no other purpose than to visit his grandchildren, what is his average mileage per gallon?

see answer page 204

THE FLIGHT OF THE PIGEONS

The pigeon fanciers' club wanted to transport their pigeons for the start of a championship race. They were against the traditional form of transport, that of keeping the birds in individual cages, for such a long journey, so they hired a special container vehicle. This was fully air conditioned, warm, well lit, large enough for the birds to fly around in and rigged out with nest boxes and perches.

The birds looked quite content as they were individually loaded into the container, quietly sitting in rows, side by side along the perches. Over 100 birds were on board when the truck set off on its journey

As it pulled away, one club member asked a question that puzzled everyone concerned. If the truck drove over a pothole in the road and frightened the birds to the extent that they all took flight at the same time, would the total weight of the truck and the cargo be less than when all the birds sat on their perches?

see answer page 204

A prospector arrived in the Klondike to stake his claim. He brought with him half a mile of rope with which to form the boundaries of the claim. Being an educated man, he knew that he could enclose the greatest area by forming the rope into a circle. This he did, but he soon ran into trouble with the authorities. The land he had claimed was larger than the maximum allowed, and he was ordered to reduce the area by half. Not wishing to fall foul of the authorities again but still wanting the maximum area he was allowed, he formed the claim into a different shape, but still used the full half mile of rope.

What shape did the prospector's claim finally take, and how many acres did it cover?

see answer page 204

WALKING THE PLANK

The greatest weight or mass that can be supported by a wooden plank of a given thickness varies directly with the variation in width and inversely with the variation in length.

A plank which is 20cm wide and 15m long can support 200kg.

What weight will a plank which is 30cm wide and 20m long support?

see answer page 204

DIGITAL CROSSWORD

This little game is, as the title suggests, a crossword with a difference. Rather than use words to complete the grid we use numbers. The rules are simple. Each clue, either across or down gives a total of the addition of the numbers on the grid in that particular row or column. You must find the numbers that add up to that total. All the numbers must be integers. Numbers may only be used once anywhere on the grid. Negative numbers are not allowed, nor it the number 0.

Clues Across
c) 37
f) 64
h) 47
i) 32

Clues Down
a) 26
b) 64
d) 31
e) 15
g) 55

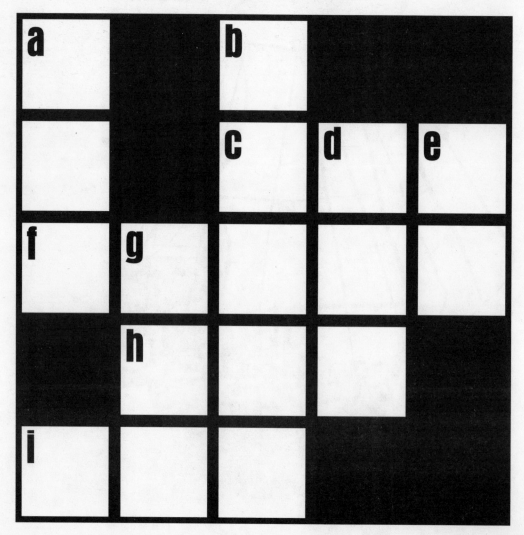

see answer page 204

PLAYING ON THE SWINGS

When my son was a little boy it was one of my pleasures to take him to the local park and let him have a ride on the swings. One day after such a ride, when I had been pushing him ever higher, he asked:

'When I was at the highest point, how far did the swing travel to the highest point at the other side.'

This I thought would be a useful conundrum to include in this collection so . . . If the ropes of the swing were 3.6 m long, and the seat when stationary was 60 cm above the ground, the highest point of the arc of the swing was just above my head, say 1.8 m.

How far did the swing travel to the highest point at the other side?

see answer page 205

THE INFINITE STADIUM

Imagine, if you can, a stadium with an infinite number of seats. Such a place can be full and still accommodate more spectators. The manager simply moves the person in Seat 1 into Seat 2, the person in Seat 2 into Seat 3, and so on. Each spectator occupies a seat with a higher number than before, and Seat 1 remains vacant for the next late arrival.

On one particular day, as the game is about to start, a coach arrives with an infinite number of passengers all wanting seats in the shortest possible time.

How does the manager deal with this situation?

see answer page 205

THE WITCH'S POLYHEDRON

The number five was regarded as very unlucky during the Middle Ages, as it was thought to represent the five wounds inflicted at the Crucifixion and the five points of the pentacle, believed to be a symbol used by witches in 'black magic'. Even the sight of a pentacle or pentagram was enough to fill people with fear and foreboding. The crystal ball was another of the witches' instruments of magic, and the combination of the crystal ball with the five-pointed figure was the ultimate in mystical power.

One particular witch had such an instrument, a crystal ball that had been fashioned into a polyhedron, each face of the polyhedron taking the shape of a regular pentagon. The local people believed this witch could foretell not only the future but many other things simply by looking into the different faces of the magical implement. Indeed, it was widely believed that she could capture the souls of unsuspecting victims, who would be entombed forever within the confines of the crystal.

Now we live in more enlightened and possibly more mundane times, and such an instrument would be to us merely an interesting geometrical shape. But please bear in mind, if you ever come across a crystal polyhedron with faces in the shape of the pentagon, treat it with respect, for it may contain the soul of one of your ancestors.

How many faces would the crystal have, and what is its geometrical name?

see answer page 205

NUMERICAL CODE

Many types of code have been developed over the years for the passing of messages. The obvious purpose of these codes is to protect the message from being intercepted by anyone other than the intended recipient. The most common form of code is one that allocates numbers to letters of the alphabet so that the sender simply writes words as a series of numbers. The only problem with this method is that the receiver must have the correct number to the letter sequence in order to decipher the message.

There is one numerical code that does not need the recipient to memorize any special sequence. It does, however, require the use of a numerical instrument. I have written a sentence below with the last word in code. It is a nine-letter word, and each integer represents a letter.

Can you decipher the word?

'You may say the last word of this sentence is 378163771.'

see answer page 205

NOUGHTS AND CROSSES (Tic-Tac-Toe)

The game of noughts and crosses has been played for centuries. This game is different. Instead of the players trying in turn to complete a line of either all noughts or all crosses, the winner is the person who can fill the bottom line of the matrix with a combination of noughts and crosses that logically completes the array.

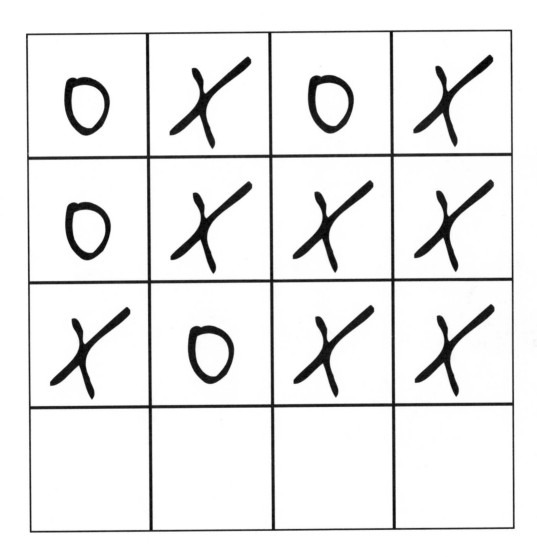

see answer page 205

STONE-THROWING

any small boys enjoy throwing stones into water. Indeed, when a group of boys are near a lake or the ocean, it is unusual not to find at least one of them throwing pebbles into the water. One such boy took his pebble-throwing very seriously and practiced daily to improve his technique. He found that it was not only the speed of the stone that gained maximum distance but that the angle of the throw was also an important factor. He found the best angle of throw to be 45°, and he estimated the greatest speed he could achieve was 30 m per second.

He arranged a contest between himself and his friends, and putting all his theory into practice he threw his stone the greatest distance.

How far did he throw the stone?

see answer page 205

MUSKET BALLS

Ammunition for muskets and flintlock pistols was usually made of lead. The making of lead shot was a simple matter. Each soldier was issued with a ladle and a mold, and they would make their own ammunition from lead obtained by collecting spent shot from the battlefield or scrounged from the local population. They would melt the lead over the campfire and pour it into the mold with the use of the ladle. Each mold could make three musket balls at once.

One resourceful soldier had the idea of making his own ladle from a section of the barrel of an old musket the same caliber as his own. By cutting a small section of the barrel, blocking one end with clay and using a length of wire for the handle, the new ladle was made. By trial and error the soldier fashioned the length of the cylindrical bowl of the ladle so that it was able to hold the exact amount of molten lead needed to make the three musket balls. This saved time and reduced the risk of spillage. Obviously, the diameter of the bowl of the ladle was the same as the diameter of the musket ball, but what length did the soldier make it?

see answer page 205

MISSING WORD

Many word puzzles are based on letters that end one word and start another, and many puzzles have been written in which the solver is asked to find the missing derivative. I've decided to include such a puzzle in this collection of conundrums to provide an interlude between the number puzzles.

In order to make it more interesting I have given you the privilege of first finding the words and then finding the connection. The rules are simple. Below are eight clues from which eight separate words can be found. When this has been done, find a three-letter word, which, when added to the end of the first four words and to the beginning of the last four, combines to form eight new words. The clues are:

1. **To protect.**

....

2. **Respond to stimulus.**

....

3. **Change your ways.**

....

4. **Rely on.**

....

5. **Contains hydrogen (usually).**

....

6. **To undergo mental anguish.**

....

7. **Run away for union.**

....

8. **The female person.**

....

see answer page 205

NUMBERS FOR LETTERS

This puzzle asks you to give a value to each of four letters. The letters are P, Q, R and S. They have been put into a matrix and the sum of each row and each column has been calculated. Your job is to find the number assigned to each of the given letters.

P	Q	R	S	119
P	P	S	S	90
Q	R	R	P	143
S	S	Q	R	112
102	119	136	107	

Do you, as I sometimes do, grow weary of puzzles involving a series of numbers? 'Not another series problem!' I can almost hear the cries of dismay from here. Wait, don't turn the page just yet; read on. This is a series you can really get to grips with – not one of the mundane prime-number variations or the arithmetic or geometric progression type. This is different.

Below is a series of letters written in a particular order. Each letter follows the last for a unique, logical reason. All you have to do is to find that reason and so find the next letter(s) in the listing. The letters are:

BCNOF?

see answer page 206

Mental arithmetic is always a good way of exercising the little grey cells. With the constant use of the electronic calculator, people are becoming less and less skilful in this department. What used to be regarded as an easy calculation is today becoming a major problem if a calculator is not available. This next puzzle – and I ask you to solve it without the use of a calculator – is very straightforward. Below is a row of numbers. Using the signs for addition, subtraction, multiplication and division once each in the spaces between the numbers, complete the operation.

$$2 \ldots 3 \ldots 4 \ldots 5 \ldots 6 = 10$$

THE INACCESSIBLE OBJECT

In school we are taught how to calculate the height of objects by using the well-proven methods of Pythagoras or by trigonometry. Both methods, as we know, make use of right-angled triangles. This is all very well in the classroom, but out in the real world things are not always that straightforward. There is almost never a clear line from the base of the object to a suitable distance for accurate measurement. The object to be measured is very rarely at 90° to the ground, and sometimes we cannot even reach the object to begin to collect the required data. The next conundrum involves such a problem and puts all those many hours of schoolwork into practice.

A surveyor needs to find the height of a rock formation, which is located at the other side of a river. He has no method of crossing the river and no way of measuring its width at that point. All he has with him is an instrument for measuring angles and a 50 m tape measure.

How does the surveyor calculate the height of the rocks?

see answer page 206

EXTRA LETTER

Many people prefer word games to number puzzles, so I have tried to cater for all tastes by including a few in this collection of conundrums. My next mind-twister uses a quotation, and is very apt to the dedicated puzzle solver who is constantly having his concentration interrupted.

Below is a six by six matrix containing the quotation. It starts at one corner and moves from letter to letter in any direction except diagonally. To make the puzzle more interesting I have inserted an extra letter at the end of the quotation (so there are 36 letters given, but the quote only contains 35). Sneaky? Well, you don't want it to be too easy, do you?

Which is the letter that does not form part of the sentence?

I	D	A	N	D	L
A	E	E	W	T	E
M	T	W	H	A	N
O	D	S	O	C	B
O	G	H	V	E	E
B	E	R	E	L	C

TRIANGLES

We are taught that all triangles have angles that add together to give 180°. No exceptions, we are told. But I am thinking of a triangle that exists in the real world, that has two base angles of 90° each, all of whose three sides are straight lines, and yet two of the sides meet at the apex to form a third angle.

What or where is this triangle?

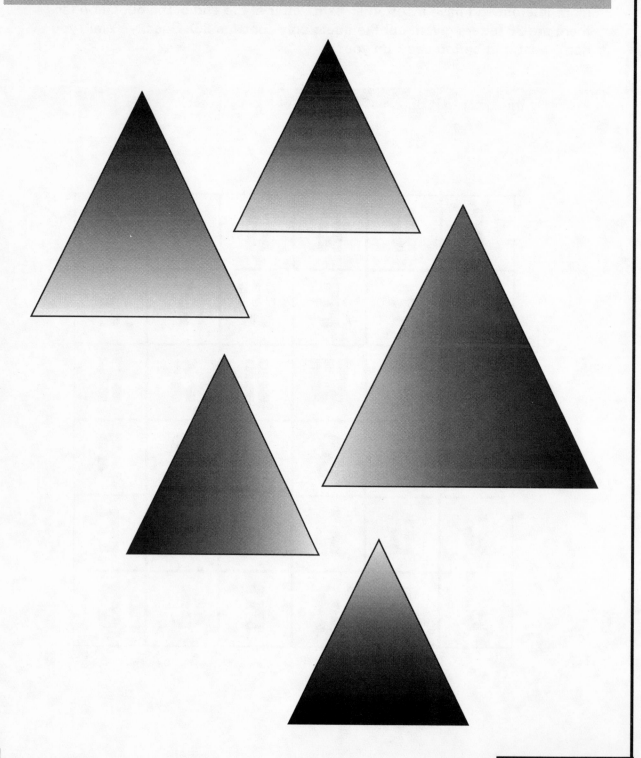

see answer page 206

YOU CAN'T TAKE IT WITH YOU

Mrs Avarice was a very rich and very miserable old lady. She refused to accept the fact that she could not take her riches with her when she threw off her mortal coil and passed over to the next world. She hated all her relatives and was too mean to give anything to charity, so she devised a plan of campaign. She instructed the executor of her will that in the event of her death all her assets were to be liquidated and the money placed in her coffin alongside her body. Her wish was for the coffin and its contents then to be cremated.

Eventually the old lady died and the executor proceeded to follow her instructions. The family, who believed they were to inherit a fortune, contested the will on the grounds that the old lady was not of sound mind when the will was made. The matter was referred to the courts. The judge presiding over the case asked for further evidence of the deceased's state of mind when the will was made. All the evidence suggested that the old lady knew exactly what she was doing at that time. After hearing the evidence the judge retired to his chambers to consider the matter.

After much deliberation, the judge ruled that the last wishes of the deceased must be paramount. He was, however, also sympathetic to the heirs of the estate and finally passed a judgement that satisfied the wishes of the deceased and delighted the family.

What did the judge order to be done?

see answer page 206

THE HAUNTED HOTEL

The manager of a remote hotel in the mountains had reports of strange figures appearing in certain rooms at certain times of year — good for business, as guests would arrive hoping for a visitation. On the other hand, it was bad for business, as the guests fled in terror after a figure had reportedly been seen floating through walls and generally causing a nuisance.

The manager had an idea. If he could predict which room was to have a visitation he could warn the guests in that room beforehand. This gave the guests the opportunity to leave or stay without a mass exodus from the hotel.

He monitored the sightings and found that from January to March Room 3 was haunted every other night. April through to June Room 4 was haunted every third night. July, August and September Room 9 became the target for the ghostly apparition, but only every fourth night. He was puzzled by this sudden jump from Room 4 to Room 9 and tried throughout the summer to figure out which room the specter would visit next and on which nights it would appear. Can you help?

see answer page 206

THE USED CAR

Fast Buck Joe, the used car salesman, bought a well-used car and then sold it for 30% profit. The poor unsuspecting person who bought the car was happy with the vehicle until it started breaking down three months later. The disgruntled customer went back to Fast Buck Joe and demanded his money back. Joe refused because of the the length of time the car had been out of his possession, but he offered to buy back the car at 20% less than the customer had paid for it. The customer reluctantly agree.

What percentage of profit did Joe make on the overall deal?

see answer page 206

THE SHEPHERD AND HIS SHEEP

A shepherd is planning to build a rectangular enclosure for his sheep, using an existing wall for one side of it. He uses pieces of pre-made fencing, each 2 m in length, and will not allow any overlap of the sections. The width of the enclosure must be greater than 20 m and the length greater than 40 m. He has only 45 sections of fence.

What size should he build the structure to enclose the greatest possible area?

see answer page 207

THE GAMBLER

Mr Mensaman was attending a convention in Las Vegas when he thought he would try his luck at the tables. The convention took place over four days, and he visited the casino every evening. Each time he arrived at the casino he had to pay an entrance fee of $100, and each time he left he gave the cloakroom attendant a $10 tip. Every evening, unlucky Mr Mensaman lost exactly half of what he started with, and went home after four days with only $10 in his pocket.

How much did Mr Mensaman have at the start of the four days?

see answer page 207

THE BUS DRIVER

Two young men boarded the city bus and approached the driver. 'One to the city center, please,' the first man said.

The driver duly gave him the ticket, and the next man approached.

'A short back and sides, please,' said the second man.

'What?' said the puzzled bus driver.

'A crew cut, then,' the man said, unperturbed by the bus driver's apparent lack of comprehension.

'Sorry,' replied the driver.

'Well just a little off the top with a few highlights if you think that is better.'

The driver was lost for words. The first man, on seeing the driver's lack of understanding, spoke up.

'I must apologize for my friend,' he said; 'he only speaks Hairdo.'

The problem over, the bus driver continued on his way.

In the bus driver's cash tin was a certain sum of money made up of 10-cent coins and twice as many five-cent coins. If the number of 10-cent coins were doubled and the number of five-cent coins decreased by 10, the sum of money would be increased by $1.10.

What was the original number of five-cent coins?

see answer page 207

TOUCHING CIRCLES

There has been a lot of publicity in recent years about the appearance of corn circles. Having seen one of these circles for myself, I am convinced that most of them are not man-made. Some of the designs and the precision with which the circles are formed make it difficult to believe that anyone using crude instruments and working in complete darkness could form these patterns in one night. But then again I am a believer in the supernatural.

My next conundrum does not, unfortunately, involve the supernatural, but it does involve circles. Three circles of different diameters touch externally. Their centers form a triangle whose sides are 5 cm, 6 cm and 9 cm respectively.

Can you find the radii of the three circles?

see answer page 207

THE NEWS VENDOR

TThis next puzzle involves newspapers and could be something to think about as you take your daily constitutional. A newsagent sells three newspapers, the Echo, the Moon and the Advertizer. He sells 70 copies of the Echo, 60 of the Moon and 50 of the Advertizer.

17 customers buy both the Echo and the Moon, 15 buy both the Moon and the Advertizer and 16 buy both the Echo and the Advertizer. Three customers buy all three papers.

How many customers does the news vendor have?

see answer page 207

WEATHER CHANGES

When we look back at the summers of our childhood we only remember the good days and forget the dull, dismal, rainy days when we sat in our rooms, bored out of our minds, and stared endlessly out of the rain-splattered window. We probably remember only half a dozen sunny days from each summer, which merge together to form one long, hot, sunny memory.

I have recently collected data on the changes in the weather where I live, and have arrived at the following possibilities for the month of June. If it is fine today, the probability that it will be fine tomorrow is 3/4. If it is wet today, the probability that it will be fine tomorrow is 1/3. Today is Thursday, and the weather is warm and sunny. I plan to go walking on Sunday.

What is the probability that Sunday will be a fine day?

see answer page 207

THE SUM OF THE PARTS

It has been stated that a person's personality is often shaped by their name. I'm not sure that I agree with this. I think it is far more probable that a person's choice of occupation or profession has been suggested by a link with their lifelong handle. I have known personally a Mr Burns the Fireman, a Mrs Sheen the cleaner and a Mr Hedges the gardener. I am sure that somewhere in the world there will be a Mr B. Troot the greengrocer and Phil McCavity the dentist. The point is that every thing and everybody is the result of the combination of many different components.

The next puzzle is a variation on the sum of two parts. The cost of making a table is calculated by adding two variables. One is proportional to the area and the other to the square of the length. If the cost of a table 2 m by 3 m is $50 and the cost of a table 1.5 m by 4 m is $64, what is the cost of a table that is 2.5 m square?

see answer page 207

ONE MAN AND HIS DOG

A farmer took his dog with him everywhere he went; they were great friends and almost inseparable. One day the farmer had to check on his flock of sheep, which was grazing on pastures three miles from the farmhouse. He set off on the three-mile walk across the open moorland with the faithful old hound close at his heels. On arrival at the pasture he checked and rechecked the sheep. Convincing himself that all was well, he eventually started his journey home. The dog knew instinctively where they were going and ran on ahead all the way back to the farmhouse. Finding the farmhouse door closed, the dog ran back to meet the farmer. When the dog reached the farmer it immediately turned and ran back to the farmhouse. The dog continued running backward and forward between the farmer and the farmhouse until they both reached home together.

Assuming the farmer walks at a speed of two miles per hour, and the dog can run at six miles per hour,

How far did the dog run on its journey home?

see answer page 207

THE PRINCE AND THE PRINCESS

Many years ago in adjacent kingdoms lived a prince and a princess who were ideally suited. They planned to marry one day, but their plans of happiness together came to a sudden end when the two kingdoms declared war on each other. From that day on they were forbidden to see or communicate with each other. To ensure the king's command was obeyed they were locked in a secure tower and guarded night and day.

One day the prince persuaded the guard to deliver and collect written messages from himself and the princess. For this service he would be paid handsomely provided he did not tell anyone about the arrangement. The guard agreed. The prince, however, did not trust the guard not to read the letters, which were for the princess's eyes only. Even if he were to seal the letters, the guard could open, read and reseal them without the princess knowing. This problem was overcome when the prince devised a way of securing the letters that made it impossible for the guard to read them before they were delivered.

How did he do it?

see answer page 207

CHICKENS AND DUCKS

Old Farmer Giles finds that there is a demand for free-range eggs in the local village. To fill this demand he decides to start keeping poultry in his farmyard. He estimates the maximum number of birds he can accommodate is 25, and he is willing to invest $80 in livestock.

Off he goes to market with the $80 tucked safely in his pocket. On arrival he finds chickens are selling at $4 each and ducks are on offer at $2 each. Speaking to more experienced poultry farmers, he finds he can expect at least five eggs per week from each chicken but only four eggs per week from each duck.

How many of each bird should he buy to obtain as many eggs per week as possible?

see answer page 207

A sheet-metal worker has a piece of metal that is 80 cm square. He needs to make an open box that has the greatest possible volume. He cuts equal square pieces from each corner of the sheet and the remaining piece is bent to form an open box.

What size would the box need to be to obtain the maximum possible volume and how much would it hold?

see answer page 208

THE CAR PARK

Up to 6,000 m^2 of land is available to build a car park for cars and small trucks. The local government has stipulated five conditions that must be met before the project can be put before the planning committee for approval:

a. There must be at least 50 spaces for trucks.
b. Each car must be allocated a minimum space of 15 m^2.
c. Each truck must be allocated a minimum space of 30 m^2.
d. The car park must have at least twice as many spaces for cars as for trucks.
e. Cars must be charged $2 per hour and trucks $5 per hour.

If these conditions are met, the committee will need to know:

1. What is the largest number of vehicles the car park could hold?
2. What number of car spaces and truck spaces will actually be provided in order to generate maximum revenue?

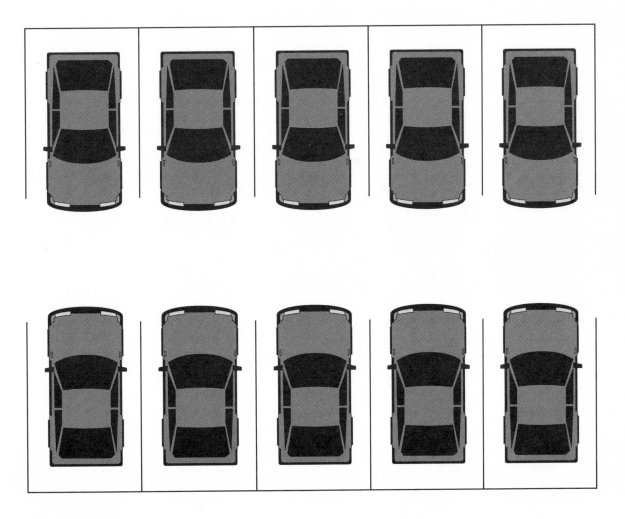

see answer page 208

THE TILER'S DILEMMA

Mr Fixit needed to tile a small section of his kitchen. When he visited the local do-it-yourself store, he found there were two sizes of tiles that suited his needs. Both sizes of tile were perfectly square, but the first tile was 2 cm smaller in length and width than the other.

He calculated that he would need only 63 of the larger tiles to cover the area he required, but he would need another 49 if he were to choose the smaller tile.

What are the sizes of the two tiles?

see answer page 208

This little problem is for the less mathematically minded readers among you and is a pleasant change from the number-crunching exercises that have dominated most of the last few pages. There have been many word puzzles that give a famous phrase or saying, leaving out the vowels and asking the puzzle solver to find the sentence. This puzzle is slightly different. This time you are given the vowels and are asked to fill in the consonants.

Below is a famous Shakespearean quotation with only the vowels in place. What is the complete quotation and from which famous play is it taken?

I _ _ U _ I _ _ E _ _ E _ OO _ O _ _ O _ E, _ _ A _ O _ .

A PILE OF BRICKS

Have you ever wondered about the mysteries of arithmetic? Does 1 + 1 always = 2? Suppose I dig a hole in the ground and then dig a second hole immediately alongside it. If I then add the two holes together by removing the dividing wall, I end up with only one hole, bigger I admit, but still only one hole.

Say I have a pile of bricks in one corner of my yard and another pile of bricks in the opposite corner of my yard. If I add the two piles together, I end up, again, with only one pile of bricks. So it must be true that in a lot of cases 1 + 1 = 1. All this has absolutely nothing to do with the next problem except it has brought bricks into the conversation.

A young lad started work on the local building site. His first job was to stack a pile of bricks, which had been tipped, randomly, from the back of a truck. He was told that each stack must contain the same number of bricks and must be no more than eight bricks high. He tried stacking them in equal piles of two high, then three, then four, then five, then six, but each time he found he had one brick left over. He finally found that by stacking them in equal piles of seven he had no bricks remaining.

How many bricks were in the original pile?

see answer page 208

THE LION, THE DONKEY AND THE CARROTS

Once upon a time there was a lion traveling south for the winter. On his journey he met a traveler leading a donkey with a sack of carrots tied to its neck.

'Greetings,' said the lion; 'are you going far?'

'Just to the other side of the river,' replied the traveller.

'Do you mind if I walk with you?' asked the lion. 'I'm going that way myself, and I will need some help to cross the river. I cannot steer the boat by myself you see.'

'You can walk with us by all means, but please don't stare at my donkey with that hungry look in your eyes.'

The three continued on their way without incident until they came to the river. They walked along the bank a little way until they found a small boat. This was the only means of transport across the river, but the boat was very small, only large enough to take two of them across at a time (and not the load of carrots), and the traveler was the only one who could steer it.

'Take me across first,' said the lion.

'I can't leave the donkey alone with those carrots,' replied the traveler. 'There will be none left by the time I return.'

'Then take the carrots first,' said the lion with a gleam in his eye.

'Then I would have no donkey left when I returned, would I?'

How did they all cross the river safely, without the lion harming the donkey or the donkey eating the carrots?

see answer page 208

COUNTING SHEEP

One of the many problems facing farmers who rear grazing animals is keeping them fed at all times. You may think that during the summer months when the grass is growing this should not be a problem. The food supply replenishes itself. However, this is a problem in itself. How quickly will the grass grow? Will the animals eat the grass more quickly than it grows? How many animals will a field of pasture feed and for how long? These are some of the many problems that are a constant worry to the farmer. He has to assess continually the pastures, the weather, the growth rate of the grass, etc., in order to keep a constant food supply for his animals.

Here is a typical problem that sheep farmers face: 15 sheep eat 10 acres of grass in 18 weeks. Provided that the grass grows at a uniform rate, how many sheep can an area of 36 acres support for 18 weeks?

see answer page 208

THE MERCILESS CAPTAIN

The two principalities of Catania and Dognia had been at war with each other off and on for centuries. At the time of this incident an uneasy peace existed between them. In order to promote harmony between the two peoples, the leaders passed a law that all merchant shipping must be manned by equal numbers from each nationality.

One fateful day such a ship set sail. The crew consisted of 30 men: 15 Catanians and 15 Dognians. The captain, a cruel and heartless man, was a strong Dognian patriot. Before very long the ship ran into a dreadful storm and suffered considerable damage. The captain decided that the only way to save the ship was to lighten the load by throwing half the crew into the sea. In order for the choice to be seen to be fair the unfortunate crew members would be chosen by lots. The method agreed upon was that all the crew members would stand in line and the captain would count along the lines in nines. Every ninth crew member would be thrown into the sea.

How did the captain organize the line-up so that it was always a Catanian and never a Dognian who was in the ninth place?

see answer page 208

FEEDING THE NEEDY

The relief truck arrived at the village to distribute much-needed food. The small village had a population of exactly 100 people. The truck contained 100 loaves of bread, and the food was about to be distributed evenly when the proceedings were suddenly stopped by the village chieftain.

'The elders of the village will make the decision on how the food will be divided,' he said in a loud booming voice.

The relief workers stopped, not wanting a confrontation, and waited for the decision from the council of elders. After a short while, the chieftain approached the truck. 'Each child will receive half a loaf of bread, each woman two loaves and each man three,' bellowed the chieftain.

'But we may not have enough to go round in those proportions,' argued a relief worker.

'You have 100 loaves?' asked the chief.

'Yes,' replied the worker.

'Then that is enough.'

How many men, women and children lived in the village?

see answer page 208

WHAT, NO PI?

Have you ever wondered if the advancement of knowledge would ever have been inhibited if Pi (3.142), the ratio of the circumference of a circle to its diameter, had never been discovered? Would we still be unable to find the area of a circle without it? To this end I offer you this challenge.

Imagine, if you will, that you are a native villager, living in the remotest region on earth. You have had no contact with civilization, but you have developed basic arithmetic skills. You also have a crude measuring stick, but the value of Pi or even its existence is unknown to you. You need, for whatever reason, to find the area of a wheel on the ground in front of you. You can measure quite accurately the diameter of the wheel. You can even find its circumference by rolling it one complete revolution and measuring the distance travelled, but can you calculate the area of the wheel?

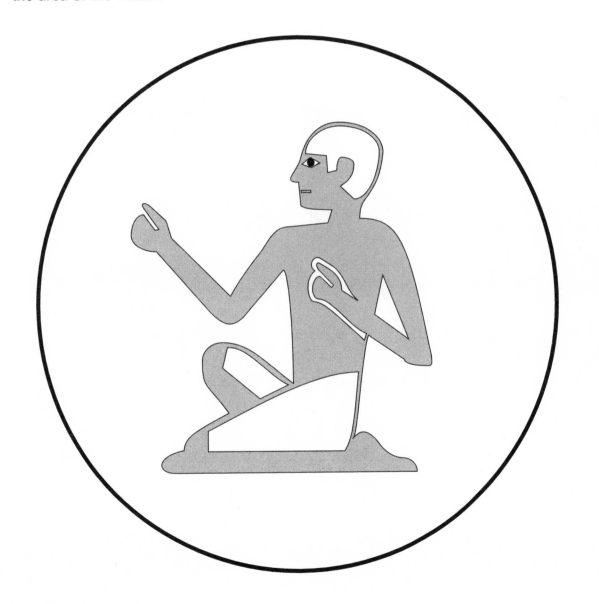

see answer page 208

CATCH ME IF YOU CAN

John Pedlar, a keen cyclist, sets off on his bike one day on a prearranged journey. His head is full of the important things in life for a teenager, such as girls, pop music, football and clothes. Forty minutes later his father finds John has forgotten something crucial for the journey. Father decides to follow John in his car and catch him before he arrives at his destination.

Now John can ride his bike at an average speed of 23 km per hour and his father drives his car at an average speed of 50 km per hour.

How far will John have travelled before his father catches him?

see answer page 208

SLOW DOWN GEORGE!

George Docile had just started driving down the highway with his wife, on the way to a vacation in France. His wife sat nervously in the rear seat, one hand on the back of the seat in front of her.

'You're going too fast,' she snapped, her knuckles turning ever whiter as she gripped the upholstery.

'If I slow down we'll miss the ferry,' replied George humbly.

'Nonsense,' his wife snapped again, 'we have plenty of time.'

'But I've calculated the speed exactly,' snivelled George. 'It's a 140 km journey, and I'm going at the exact speed for us to arrive at the terminal exactly on time.'

'Don't you argue with me,' his wife cried as she swung her handbag at the back of George's head. 'Now slow down.'

'Yes dear, anything you say dear, you know best.'

George sighed as he slowed the car down by 14 km per hour.

All was quiet for a time as his wife dropped off to sleep. George kept the car at the lower speed for the rest of the journey, not daring to increase it in case his wife woke up. Eventually they arrived at the terminal just in time to see the ferry leaving the dock and moving slowly out to sea.

'You stupid man,' cried his wife as her handbag made contact with the back of George's head once again.

'You've made us 20 minutes late; I can't trust you to do anything right.'

How fast was George driving before he reduced speed?

THE CONFERENCE

Five major powers are to hold a meeting to discuss matters of international importance. The organizers of the meeting are faced with the task of formulating the seating arrangements. No party must be made to feel inferior to any other. There have been no objections or instructions as to who sits next to whom. Each delegation will consist of three members who must sit together. The leader of each will sit in the middle with a secretary at either side of him. The decision is made for the discussions to take place at a round table.

In how many different ways can the members be arranged around the table?

see answer page 209

CONNECTIONS

There are many words that can be connected to other words to form a completely different meaning. The word in this puzzle has only four letters, but it has at least two different meanings in its own right. It can act as a prefix to at least 12 others to form new and varied words. The meanings of these 12 words range from 'supposition' to 'the rate of breathing' and from 'insincerity' to 'part of a triangle'. The word itself can mean 'slightly' or can be a nickname for a particular chemical.

Can you name the word?

1

....

2

....

3

....

4

....

5

....

6

....

7

....

8

....

9

....

10

....

11

....

12

....

see answer page 209

THE HOCKEY TEAM

The manager of the local hockey team has the unenviable task of selecting the players. The team is always made up of five men and six women. The club has seven male members and nine female members all of equal ability. As usual everybody wants to be in the first team. He tries his best to be impartial in his selection, but is always accused of favoritism by the people left out.

Throughout the season the manager tries to make sure everyone plays at least once in the first team and also endeavors to try all the combinations of players in order to find the most effective winning team.

How many games will the team have to play to ensure every club member plays in the first team at least once and all team combinations have been tried?

see answer page 209

THE ASTRONAUT

One of the problems that an astronaut has to deal with is weightlessness, which I imagine might not be unpleasant. What I *do* believe might be unpleasant is gaining weight again on return to earth: having to feel your limbs becoming heavier and heavier as you approach the earth.

The weight of an astronaut varies inversely as the square of his distance from the center of the earth. If we take the radius of the earth as 6370 km, at what height above the surface of the earth will the astronaut's weight be 1/10 of his weight on earth?

see answer page 209

TAKE A HIKE

Agroup of walkers hiked from Town A to Town B at an average speed of four miles an hour, and then back from Town B to Town A at a speed of one mile an hour. The outward journey took one hour less than the return.

How far did they walk on the round trip?

see answer page 209

A DRIVE TO THE MED

Mr White felt he needed a holiday in the sun, so he took his family on a motoring trip to the south of France. The distance from the English Channel to the Mediterranean is 1,200 km. His car will travel an average distance of 9 km per liter of fuel and 600 km to a liter of oil. He calculated the cost of the journey to be $85.

On the way his fuel consumption was as he expected, but he had to buy an extra liter of oil, which he paid for, as he did for his fuel, in French francs. On his arrival, at the Mediterranean coast, he found he had spent the equivalent of $87.60 on fuel and oil.

What was the average price per liter of the fuel he used?

see answer page 209

THE FISH POND

Mr Brown is building himself a fishpond in his back garden. He has dug a circular hole 3 m in diameter and 1 m deep. The sides of the hole are as vertical as he can make them, and the bottom of the hole is perfectly level. He now needs a sheet of waterproof material in order to line the pond, allowing half a meter of overlap all the way around the top.

On his visit to the local aquatic center he finds the lining material is sold only by the square meter. He calculates the area to be covered and asks the sales assistant for 22 m^2 of material.

The assistant, who is familiar with what Mr Brown is building, says, 'That's not enough to cover the bottom of the pond, the walls and the overlap.'

'Yes it is,' replies Mr Brown. 'I've calculated it carefully.'

'Look,' says the assistant, 'Your pond is 3 m diameter, plus two walls 1 m each, plus 1/2 m each side for overlap, which makes a circle of 6 m in diameter. The area of such a circle is π x 3 x 3, which equals 28.27 m^2, so you need 29 m.'

'No, no,' cried Mr Brown, 'Looking at it from above you will see a circle of 3 m for the pond plus 1/2 m each side for overlap, making a 4 m diameter circle. Find the area of that and add it to the area of the walls you get: (π x 2 x 2) + (2 x π x 1.5 x 1) equals 21.99 m^2, so I only need 22 m.'

Who is correct?

see answer page 209

THE PRISONER

Once upon a time there was a ruthless landowner who treated his servants as slaves. One such unfortunate soul was a young man named John. He was given the task of repairing the flat roof of a stone-built out-building set in a remote area of the grounds. He worked night and day on the task in order to please his temperamental master, all to no avail. The landowner was angered by what he called the outrageous cost of the materials. He accused John of stealing and ordered him to be imprisoned in the building until he confessed to his crime.

The weeks passed as John, innocent of any wrong-doing, lay in the single roomed building. There were no windows, and the only entrance was a thick wooden door. The building was unheated, and the floor was made of solid rock. Fearing he would be entombed forever John planned his escape. His only chance was to tunnel through the stone walls. He paced his cell, in the darkness and found it measured 5 m by 4 m. He remembered the area of the roof to be 34 m^2 and he assumed all the walls would be of the same thickness.

How thick are they?

In planning the layout of a new airliner, it is proposed to install a certain number of complete rows of first-class seats and a certain number of economy-class seats. The conditions governing the installation are:

I. Each row of first-class seats occupies 1.6 m of the length of the cabin, and each row of economy-class seats occupies 1 m; the total length of cabin available is 40 m.

II. Each row of first-class seats holds 6 passengers, whereas each row of economy-class seats holds 8 passengers; the airline requires that the cabin can seat at least 192 passengers altogether.

III. Each first-class passenger is entitled to 20 kg of baggage, and each economy-class passenger is entitled to 15 kg of baggage; the total baggage carried must not exceed 3,840 kg.

What is the minimum permissible number of economy-class passengers under these conditions?

see answer page 209

HIEROGLYPHICS

It has always amazed me how experts such as Egyptologists and archaeologists can decipher the strange picture-like writing that is found on many ancient tombs. Where do they begin? How do they know for certain that their interpretation of what is written is correct? I imagine it is purely by mutual agreement between experts in the same subject that any interpretation is accepted.

For my next conundrum I ask you to test your skills in the interpretation of what appear to be hieroglyphics. Below is a series of shapes. Each one follows the last for a particular logical reason. I ask you to find the next shape in the series and explain why the symbols are the shape they are?

see answer page 209

THE SCHOOLTEACHER

Mr Jones, the schoolteacher, had an obsession for fine ball-point pens. He had many in his collection, but he only used four of them for work. Each of these pens contained a different colored ink. Sometimes he only took one pen to work, sometimes two, sometimes three and occasionally all four. He tried to take a different combination of pens to school with him each day.

For how many consecutive days can he take a different selection of pens to work?

see answer page 209

SHARE AND SHARE ALIKE

Five tramps agreed to meet one evening and share evenly the amount of food and cash each of them had manged to acquire during the day. The first had three loaves of bread, but no cash. The second had two loaves of bread and $1.50. The third had one loaf and $3. The fourth had half a loaf and $3.75. The fifth had no bread but $4.50. Rather than simply pool their spoils and divide it between them, the men with the bread sold it to the men without bread until each man had equal amounts of bread and money.

What was their price for a loaf of bread?

see answer page 209

THE SHEEP RANCH

Lucky Mr Thrifty inherited a sheep ranch in Australia. The documents sent to him by the local attorney described the land as a triangular section, bounded by straight lines joining three small towns. Town B was directly west of town A, while town C lay somewhere between the two, but several miles to the north. The distance between A and B was 12 miles, between A and C 17 miles and between B and C 14 miles.

Having no wish to emigrate to Australia Mr Thrifty instructed the solicitor to sell the land at a price of $1,000 per square mile.

How much money can he expect to receive from the sale of the land?

76

see answer page 210

FUEL PRICES

In a world of ever-increasing prices we all have to make economies from time to time. Mr Thrifty was more eager than most to do this.He decided that every time the price of fuel was increased by a certain percentage, he would decrease his annual mileage by the same amount, and he would keep careful records of his mileage and the amount he spent. When the last increase of five cents in the dollar came into effect, Mr Thrifty decreased his annual mileage by the same percentage and took a note of his mileage and expenditure.

After a year he compared his expenditure on fuel to the previous year and to his surprise found that he had saved $2.

What was his annual fuel bill before the increase?

TAKE THE TRAIN

Modernization of the transport systems is a continuous process, with the main emphasis on decreasing journey time. Trains are now probably the fastest form of travel for medium-length journeys, although getting to the nearest station is still a time-consuming business.

On average, trains can now cover the same distance in 3/4 of the original time.

How much faster do trains now travel as a fraction of their original speed?

see answer page 210

THE JOGGER

Mr Smith's place of employment is nine miles from his home. One day he decides to jog to work in order to increase his fitness. He estimates the journey time to be a little over 1 hour 45 minutes. As he sets off the village clock strikes 7 a.m.

At first he feels fine, but before long his energy begins to fade and he realizes he will not be able to run the whole distance. A passing cab is the answer to his prayer. Mr Smith hails the cab and completes his journey, arriving at work one hour 10 minutes earlier than he had anticipated.

Assuming Mr Smith could run at 1/6 the speed of the cab, how far did he run before he hailed the taxi?

see answer page 210

'I am almost three times as old as my son,' the bartender sighed as he pulled a pint of draught beer.

'Well, none of us is getting any younger,' the man across the bar replied with a degree of sympathy.

'No,' agreed the bartender, 'but it makes me feel better knowing that in 12 years' time I'll only be twice his age.'

'Really!' exclaimed the customer. 'How old are you now then?'

'Ah, that would be telling,' grinned the bartender. 'Work it out for yourself.'

Another customer, overhearing the conversation between the bartender and the first customer, butted in. 'When you've solved that problem, see if you can figure out my age. Eight years ago I was eight times the age of my daughter. Now if you add our ages together they come to 52 years. If you can figure that one out, I'll buy you your next drink.'

see answer page 210

STILL IN THE BAR

Some time later, as the bar was closing and the bartender was collecting the empty bottles, he complained to his wife, 'Why do we have to return all these bottles to the brewery? Why can't we just throw them away?'

'Each bottle with its top costs eight cents to make,' replied his wife. 'That's why we have to return them.'

'But we throw the tops away. How much do they cost to make?'

'I don't know, but the bottle costs six cents more than the top. You figure it out.'

see answer page 210

A number containing two digits is increased by 54 when the digits are reversed. If the sum of the digits is 12, what is the number?

A number containing two digits is such that twice the 10 digit is greater than the unit digit by six. When the digits are reversed the number is increased by nine. What is the number?

A number with three digits has the hundred digits three times the unit digit, and the sum of the digits is 19. If the digits are written in reverse order the value of the number is decreased by 594. What is the number?

see answer page 210

struggling university student, Ivor Nodosh, needs to earn extra cash to subsidize his scholarship. During the summer vacation he manages to obtain temporary work as a shelf-stacker in the local supermarket. His employer, having experience of poor attendance from students he has hired in the past, employs him under certain conditions. Ivor must work for five days a week over a four-week period. He will be paid $25 for every day he works, but will have $10 deducted for every day he fails to attend. He will be paid in a lump sum at the end of the period, provided he attends work on that day.

Ivor works hard for most of the time, but as the days pass his enthusiasm begins to fade and he fails to attend work on several occasions. He does, however, manage to attend on the last day and receives a payment of $395 before deductions.

How many days did he fail to turn up for work?

see answer page 210

The apartment where Ivor Nodosh lives while at university consists of two rooms. Both rooms are perfectly square, and one room is 1 ft larger in its internal dimensions than the other. The rent Ivor is charged is $1.20 per ft^2 of floor area per term.

If the rent Ivor pays is $375.60 per term, what are the internal dimensions of the room?

see answer page 210

THINK OF A NUMBER

I'm thinking of a number. I double that number, add six and multiply the result by 10. I now divide the result by 20 and take away the number I first thought of.

What is the result?

see answer page 210

I am now thinking of a two-digit number. I find that if I add the two digits together and divide them into the original number, I obtain the answer seven.

What was the number I was thinking of?

(There are four possible answers.)

see answer page 210

PARTY TIME

We invited 10 married couples to our last New Year's Eve party. When they had all arrived I found all the ladies preferred to drink spirits while the men wanted cans of beer. Having only a limited supply of drinks, I decided it would be only fair to share the cans equally between the men before the party got fully underway. To my surprise, I found that if I had invited one more couple, each man would have received one drink less and I would have been able to have one drink extra.

How many cans were shared at the party?

see answer page 210

THE BOATMAN

A boatman whose craft can travel at 6 mph in still water finds that whenever he travels upstream the journey takes twice as long as the return trip. This happens every time, regardless of the length of journey. The current of the river on which he travels is always at a constant speed.

What is the speed of the current?

see answer page 210

THE ROUND TRIP

Mr Mensaman, who resides in Southtown, has to travel to Northtown to visit his brother. He catches the 11.20 train and arrives in Northtown in time for lunch. Looking at the station clock as he disembarks, his razor-sharp brain calculates the average speed of the train to have been 72 km/h.

After spending two hours taking lunch and visiting his brother he decides to return home by bus. The route the bus takes is 2 km longer than the train journey, but it stops directly outside Southtown railway station. As Mr Mensaman steps down from the bus he confirms his time of arrival as 3.15 p.m. He calculates the speed at which the bus has been travelling and finds it to have been 40 km/h.

What is the distance between Southtown and Northtown by train?

see answer page 210

VACATION BY THE SEA

Mr Mensaman always goes to the same place for his vacation. This year, money is a little tight, so he takes with him only $420 to cover his hotel bill and spending money. He budgets his expenditure very carefully and tries to make the vacation last for as long as possible. As the money runs out and the vacation inevitably draws to a close, Mr Mensaman recalculates his finances. He finds that if he had spent $7 a day less he could have extended the vacation for another five days.

How long a vacation did he have?

see answer page 210

A DAY IN THE LIFE OF A GREENGROCER

Mr B. Troot, the greengrocer, bought a certain number of pineapples for $72, but found he could not sell the last 10% and they were wasted. The rest he sold at a profit of 8 cents per pineapple. Mr Troot found he had made a profit of $14.40 on the deal.

How many pineapples did he buy?

Mr B. Troot next bought a number of pounds of apples for $4. If they been 4 cents per pound cheaper, he could have bought 5 lb more for the same money.

How much did he pay, per pound, for the apples?

After carrying sacks of potatoes each day Mr B. Troot becomes tired and has to take a rest. On these occasions he uses the time to work out his finances. He stocks two types of potatoes, one type he buys for $1.50 per sack and the other for $1.70. He calculates that if he had bought half as many at $1.50 and twice as many at $1.70, his bill would have been $196 instead of the $188 he actually paid.

How many sacks of each type of potato did he buy?

see answer page 210

MORE AND MORE MOORES

Old Mrs Moore was having a party to celebrate her 90th birthday and needed to hire a reception hall in order to accommodate all her descendants. She invited her children and their spouses, her grandchildren and their spouses and all her great-grandchildren.

   She had three times as many grandchildren as she had children and three times as many great-grandchildren as grandchildren. 86 people in all attended the party.

How many children did Mrs Moore have?

see answer page 210

Sitting uneasily in the doctor's waiting room one day, a prospective patient stared at the clock on the wall. She had been waiting for what seemed an age.

To take her mind off the reason for her visit she started to invent little puzzles to solve.

Estimating the length of the minute hand of the clock to be 4 in, she calculated the distance the hand had travelled around the clock since she had first arrived to be 15 in.

How long had she been waiting?

COFFEE BREAK QUIZ

This brief interlude from the more studious conundrums is to provide the dedicated puzzle solver with a little relaxation before embarking on the next section of mind-straining problems. Each statement is a cryptic clue to a well-known phrase or saying. Your job, obviously, is to find the correct interpretation.

1. Sewing the herb stops one over the eight.

2. Hard pencil or soft pencil.

3. A quick leaf through his astrology magazine cheers up the sheep herder no end.

4. A quick swig won't make the sun shine.

5. Peter and Thomas hope the Captain doesn't appear and ruin the appetizer.

The next five statements are cryptic clues to the titles of Bond films.

1. The mean physician.

2. The satellite gardener.

3. Au. I.

4. The eight legged cat.

5. Stormy Dance.

And finally, in case there is a tie :

What well known event is hidden in this statement: 'the subscription to the candle makers' union'?

see answer page 210

TAKE THE TRAIN 2

From Ammington to Cadfield is 375 miles by rail. Brotherton is on the line between them and is 150 miles from Ammington. At 12.00 a train sets out from Ammington and travels to Brotherton, arriving at 13.15. It waits there for 15 minutes and then travels on to Cadfield, arriving at 15.00. Another train leaves Cadfield at 12.30 and travels non-stop to Ammington at an average speed of 100 miles per hour.

How far from Brotherton do the two trains pass each other and at what time?

see answer page 211

HOW HIGH IS THE MOUNTAIN?

The Canary Islands are known for a particular landscape feature, the Peak of Tenerife. Mountaineers who have climbed the peak are said to be able to see the coast of Africa on a clear day.

One such adventurous person took with him an instrument for measuring angles with the intention of calculating the height of the mountain for himself. On reaching the summit he accurately measured the angle of depression to the horizon and found it to be 1.97°. Taking the diameter of the earth to be 7,914 miles,

How high is the mountain?

see answer page 211

Have you ever considered how time is calculated when traveling? We have to put our clocks and watches forward if we travel west and back if we travel east. For convenience we use multiples of one hour, but this is not absolutely correct. As we travel, time must change at a uniform rate in either direction.

From this we can form a little problem, which may keep us occupied on those long boring journeys.

Today is June 21 and it is 12 noon.

What is the absolute time at a place exactly 75° west?

see answer page 211

OVER A BARREL

Barrels and casks have been made and used for centuries for the storing of many different types of liquid. Barrel-making is a highly skilled job, and the art is more or less declining as metal casks become more common. Have you ever wondered how the coopers of old knew how large to make a barrel to hold a specified amount of liquid? Nowadays with the help of calculus and modern computers there is no problem, but calculus was not developed until the late 17th century, and barrels had been in use for a long time by then. My next conundrum asks you to calculate the capacity of a barrel. Unfortunately you do not have the advantage or the opportunity to use trial and error, and neither are you allowed to use calculus or a computer. A barrel has a diameter of 24 in at its base and its head, a diameter of 32 in at the center and a height of 40 in.

How much liquid will it hold?

By the way, just to add to your vexation, I need the answer in gallons.

see answer page 211

BUBBLES IN THE BATH

hen sitting in the bath tub as a child, did you ever wonder why bubbles are round?

The scientific explanation is that a sphere holds the maximum volume for the smallest surface area. The gas inside a bubble tries to expand while the surface tension tries to contract, thus forming a sphere. Checking the theory for myself I found that if I took the volume of a sphere 2 in in diameter and divided it by the surface area, I arrived at the ratio of 1:3.

If I did the same thing, but with a 2 in cube, I arrived at the same ratio.

Was this coincidence or is the scientific explanation in doubt?

see answer page 211

CANNON BALLS

The complexity of mathematics used by our ancestors long before such things as calculators or computers were invented never ceases to amaze me. One such formula I came across recently while browsing through my collection of old books was for the calculation of the initial velocity of a projectile as it was fired from a cannon. It appears that the velocity of a cannon ball is directly proportional to the square root of the weight of the charge of gun powder and inversely proportional to the weight of the cannon ball. It is given by this formula:

V = 1600 x the square root of 3C/B where C is the weight of the charge and B is the weight of the cannon all.

Given that the velocity of a cannon ball weighing 24 lb is 800 ft per second, what would be the velocity of an 18 lb ball fired with the same charge?

see answer page 211

THE PLAYING FIELD

The local school was holding a sports day in the nearby playing field. This field was perfectly square and the ground reasonably flat. A race between the school's fastest runners was arranged. The coach wanted the race to be staged on the longest and straightest course possible, so he marked out a track along the diagonal of the field. The race was won by little Billy Wiz in a time of 28.28 seconds. The coach, pleased with the result, calculated that Billy had run at a speed of 5 m per second.

What is the area of the field to the nearest square meter?

see answer page 211

A triangular field which has one side 10 m in length is the pasture for Nanny the goat. She is tethered to a rope which is tied to a stake set into the ground. The position of the stake and the length of the rope is such that Nanny can just reach each of the boundaries of the field. Two sides of the field, which are equal in length, both form angles of 70° with the 10 m side.

What is the area of pasture available for Nanny to feed from?

see answer page 211

THE CIRCUMSCRIBED CIRCLE

The cutting tool that bores large circular holes into wood is often in the shape of an equilateral triangle with a cutting edge on each vertex. This shape of cutter is often preferred because it allows more clearance between the work piece and the tool, and yet provides perfect balance when run at high speeds. The only problem with this type of cutter is choosing the correct size tool for a particular size of hole. Being triangular in shape it cannot be measured directly across the diameter and so the size of hole it will produce has to be calculated. Such a cutter is selected and when measured between the vertices is found to be exactly 5 cm.

What is the diameter of the hole it will produce?

see answer page 211

THE BUILDER'S CONUNDRUM

A builder builds three identical detached houses beside each other. Each one requires a connection to gas, water and electricity. The local utility companies are renowned for non-cooperation with each other. All three companies agree to supply the service required for each of the houses, but only under certain conditions: the route chosen for the supply cable or pipe-work must be such that it does not cross over, at any point, either of the other two services, and the supplies must be laid below ground level. The supplies cannot pass beneath any buildings.

Can you find such a route?

see answer page 211

THERE'S A HOLE IN MY BUCKET

In my garden there is an old metal bucket in which I collect rain water to irrigate my plants. The bucket measures 20 cm at the base, 30 cm at the brim and is 25 cm deep. During a recent downpour the bucket was filled to overflowing with rainwater, but unfortunately it suddenly sprang a leak right at the bottom. It now loses water at a rate of one milliliter per second.

How long will it take for the bucket to empty, provided that it doesn't rain in the meantime?

see answer page 212

STOP THE LEAK

In order to conserve as much rainwater as I could, I tilted the bucket at an angle. The hole was located where the bottom joined the side, right in the corner. Turning it so that the hole was uppermost, I secured the bucket in such a position that the upper rim and the hole were on the same level. Last night it rained, filling my tilted bucket with as much water as it can hold in its present position.

How much water will it now hold?

(Answers in liters, please.)

see answer page 212

GOING INTO ORBIT

Have you ever wondered what the earth looks like from outer space? The view must be fantastic. I know we have all seen photographs, but I imagine these cannot compare in the slightest with the real thing. If we travelled far enough away from the earth we could see half of its surface at once, but how far must we travel away from the earth in order to see just 1/3 of its surface?

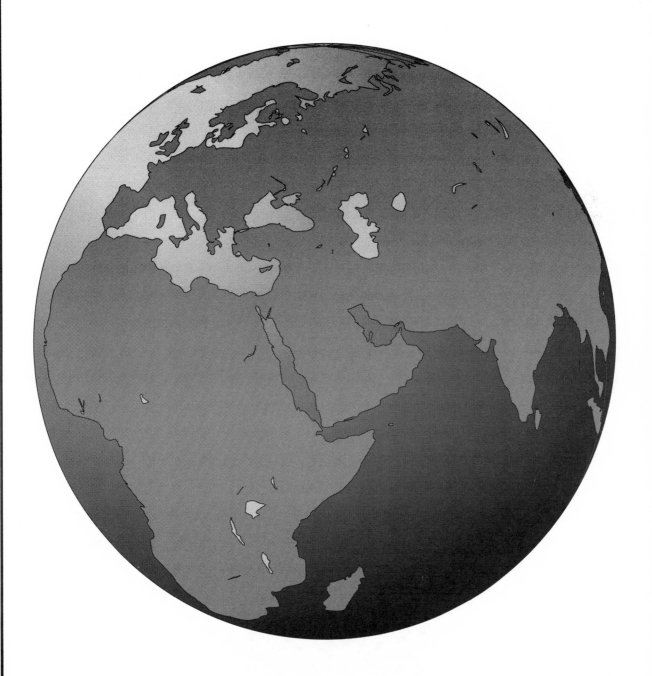

see answer page 212

THE WICKED QUEEN

Once upon a time in a land far away lived a wicked queen with an insatiable appetite for strong young men. She would take them into her palace, make use of them and then draft them into the army when she grew tired of them.

One such young man, named Sam, came to the attention of the queen. He lived on a farm with his widowed mother. The queen ordered him report to the palace the very next day. Sam's mother pleaded with the queen not to take her son. She could not run the farm alone; without him she would starve. The queen, unmoved by the mother's appeal but not wishing to seem unfair in the eyes of her courtiers, struck a bargain with her.

'Meet me, with your son, in the courtyard tomorrow,' she demanded. 'There we will put two pebbles in a bag, one black and one white, and your son will pick out one of them. If he chooses the black pebble then he is mine. If he chooses the white pebble he is yours. If he refuses to pick a pebble then you will both be charged with treason and thrown into prison.'

Next day Sam and his mother waited in the courtyard of the palace. Eventually the queen arrived with one of her attendants. Sam watched as the attendant bent down and picked up two pebbles from the gravel pathway. His keen eye noticed that the attendant placed two black pebbles into the bag. The queen then asked Sam to pick out the pebble that would determine his fate and that of his mother.

How did Sam resolve the situation?

see answer page 212

THE PENTAGON

Anyone who watches American crime series on television will be familiar with the headquarters of the American Intelligence Services. Their offices are situated in a five sided building in Washington D.C. known as The Pentagon.

Now a pentagon is one of the more difficult of the geometrical shapes to draw accurately. There are several ways to construct one inside a circle, but they are all quite complex and difficult to remember. There is a way of calculating the length of the side of a pentagon given the radius of the circle that encloses it. The formula is quite straightforward if you can find it. Once you have done that, find the length of the side of a pentagon which is enclosed in a circle 12 cm in diameter.

see answer page 212

SQUARES AND CIRCLES

A well-known trick for a surprise present at a birthday party is to buy a small item and place it in a cardboard box. The box is placed in a larger box, and that box into one which is larger still, and so on until the small present looks like a much larger one. My next conundrum involves boxes within boxes, but with a slight difference.

A box in the shape of a perfect cube with a volume of 1 liter is placed inside a globe. The diameter of the globe is such that the box fits exactly inside it. The globe is then, in turn, placed in a larger cubical box. Again it is a perfect fit.

What is the volume of the larger box?

(Ignore the thickness of the walls of the smaller box and the globe.)

see answer page 212

THE WINE GLASS AND THE CRYSTAL BALL

This next conundrum is a particularly evil one. Like all good conundrums it has the appearance of simplicity, but there is a nasty sting in the tail (or tale).

A large conical wine glass is filled to the brim with fine red wine. A perfectly spherical crystal ball is placed, gently, into the glass, causing the wine to spill over. If the diameter of the glass at the mouth is 5 in and the depth is 6 in, while the diameter of the ball is 4 in,

How much wine is spilled?

see answer page 212

WIRE IT UP

One cubic foot of copper is to be made into one continuous length of wire. This is done by heating the copper to a point where the metal is pliable and then drawing it through a series of rollers. Each pair of rollers has a circular groove around its circumference. The diameter of the groove decreases slightly with each pair of rollers so that the copper is forced through the grooves until it reaches the required diameter. Obviously the formed wire increases in length with every pair of rollers it passes through. The speed of the wire passing from roller to roller also increases as the copper is forced to become ever smaller in cross-sectional area.

For my next conundrum I ask you to find the length of wire produced from one cubic foot of copper when its diameter is reduced to 0.025 in.

(I would like the answer in miles please.)

see answer page 213

ost people who drive a car or ride a bicycle are familiar with transference of momentum via a belt or chain from one pulley or gear to another. One pulley is driven by the engine or by muscle power, and the movement is transferred to the belt, which in turn drives the second pulley. The size difference of the two pulleys determines the final speed of the second pulley.

To calculate the length of the belt between two pulleys of equal diameters we must add together the two halves of the circumferences of the pulleys and twice the center distance between them. For example, if two pulleys 15 cm in diameter are fixed 45 cm apart, then the length of belt required to connect them is found by:

$$\tfrac{1}{2} \ (2 \times 3.142 \times 15) + (2 \times 45) = 137.1$$

But can you find the length of belt required if the speed is to be increased by a ratio of 1:4? A pulley 30 cm in diameter is connected by a belt to a second pulley 7.5 cm in diameter. The centers of the two pulleys are fixed at a distance of 45 cm apart.

What is the length of the belt which connects them?

see answer page 213

BRIDGE OVER TROUBLED WATER

The little village of Soggyfoot in the mountains is famous for its picturesque village green and its large circular duck pond. The pond is 140 m in diameter and is the centerpiece of the village. The village pub and the local shops are on one side of the pond while most of the residential buildings are on the other. The residents have complained to the council about the distance the elderly have to walk around the pond to reach the shops and have campaigned for a bridge. Reluctantly the local government has agreed, but to save costs the bridge is not to pass over the center of the pond. It will be built to one side, as this is a shorter span. The proposed bridge will be positioned 1/4 of the way along the diameter of the pond, splitting the pond in a ratio of 3:1. The cost of the bridge is estimated at $100 per meter.

How much money will be saved by building the bridge in this position rather than straight across the center?

see answer page 213

THE LEGACY

When an old man died he left his 10 grandchildren a large sum of money to be divided between them. The old man had one failing in his life: he showed blatant favoritism among his descendants. This continued after his death.

The will was read and the conditions of the legacy were disclosed. A list was provided with the names of the 10 grandchildren written in order of preference. The money, $100,000 in all, was to be distributed in this order, the name at the top of the list receiving the most and the name at the bottom of the list receiving the least. There were to be even increments between the 10 so that the difference between the amounts of money each of them received was constant.

If number eight on the list received $6,000 how much did each of the other nine receive?

see answer page 213

FIELDS OF CORN

A farmer owns two fields of different sizes, in which he grows corn. Together they cover an area of 30 acres. From the first field he can reap 40 kg of corn per acre but from the second only 30 kg per acre. At harvest time he weighs the total yield from each field and finds that he has produced 500 kg more from the larger field than from the smaller.

What are the sizes of the two fields?

see answer page 213

THE THREE WISE WOMEN

Three fashion-conscious young women were down town shopping one day. They stopped and looked in the window of a shop selling hats. There in the window was a hat that each of them liked, priced at $170, but none of them had enough money left to buy it. They each examined the contents of their purses.

The first said to the other two, 'If you lend me 1/2 of what you have I can buy the hat.'

The second said to the other two, 'If you lend me a 1/3 of what you have I can buy the hat.'

'But,' the third said to the other two, 'if you loan me a 1/4 of what you have I could buy the hat.'

How much money did each of them have in their purses?

see answer page 214

FIT FOR A KING

For his coronation the King of Catania commissioned a crown to be made. It was to be embedded with diamonds, rubies and other precious stones, but his main cause of concern was the weight of it. He gave special instructions that its weight before the stones were positioned on it was to be no more than 60 oz. It was to be made from gold, platinum, silver and copper. The gold and silver together would make up 66.66 per cent of the weight, the gold and the copper 75 per cent of the weight and the gold and the platinum 60 per cent.

How much of each metal was used to make the crown?

see answer page 214

PIPES AND TANKS

A large water tank is fed from four different supplies. Each supply has a different sized pipe. The largest pipe, when running at full bore, can fill the tank in one day. The next largest can fill the tank in two days, the next in three days and the smallest in four.

How long will it take to fill the tank with all four pipes running at their maximum flow?

(Answer in hours and minutes, please)

see answer page 214

THE CHARITY WALK

A group of five people of various ages and fitness agreed to organize a sponsored walk for charity. The walk was to be in the form of a relay over a distance of 100 miles. It was agreed that each person would cover a different distance according to their ability. The oldest person would be the first to go and would walk a given distance. The next person would walk the same as the last plus a measured amount, and so on. This allowed the youngest and fittest to be the last walker and cover the greatest distance. A list of the names and distances to be covered was prepared. This was scrutinized by the group, and they discovered that the last three walkers were covering seven times the distance of the first two.

How far was each member asked to walk?

see answer page 214

THE OWL AND THE WEASEL

A wise old owl was sitting high in a treetop one moonlit night waiting for his supper to arrive. He knew that a weasel lived in a hole at the base of the tree, and he was determined that the weasel would become his evening meal. Eventually the weasel arrived at a spot which was three times the height of the tree away from the hole. The owl and the weasel's eyes met at the same instant!

The weasel made a dash for the hole. The wise old owl instantly assessed the speed at which the rodent was running and swooped down to a point of interception. When the owl grabbed the weasel they had both travelled equal distances in straight lines.

How far was the weasel from the hole when he met his fate?

see answer page 214

UNIT FRACTIONS

The ancient Egyptians regarded fractions differently than we do today. To them general fractions such as 3/4 were part of an incomplete process. They believed that all fractions, with the possible exception of 2/3, were the sum of a series of unit fractions – that is, fractions with the number 1 as the numerator, such as 1/2, 1/4, 1/3, etc. For example 2/5 can be expressed as 1/3 + 1/15, or 2/11 can be written as 1/6 + 1/66.

   My next conundrum asks you to express a fraction in the terms of two unit fractions, if you can.

If 1/x + 1/y = 2/103, find x and y when x and y are whole numbers and x does not equal y.

see answer page 214

THE SIX BROTHERS

There once was a farmer who had six sons. Each one was born exactly a year after the last. As the years went by the farmer thought it was time for the boys to learn the rudiments of crop growing, so he allocated each boy a piece of land which was proportional to their ages. He did this by dividing one of his rectangular fields with a fence which ran along the diagonal, thus forming a triangle. He then sub-divided the triangle with six fences equal distances apart, parallel to the side, which formed a right-angle with the length. The length of the triangular field was 120 m, and it covered an area of 3,000 square meters. Now each section of land was allocated to one of the brothers, the oldest receiving the largest, the next oldest receiving the next largest and so on with the youngest receiving the smallest.

Each piece of land was smaller than the one next to it by the same proportion; that is to say, the pieces of land decreased in area by a constant increment.

By how much did each section of land decrease in area?

see answer page 215

IN THE HEAT OF THE SUN

It was high noon when the truck broke down, traveling east to west on the main road that runs exactly along the equator across Africa. The red ignition light on the dashboard had been showing for some time; now the battery was completely dead, and the truck came to a standstill. Luckily the driver had his mobile phone with him, and he telephoned for help, but it was going to be several hours before anyone could reach him.

The sun blazed down making the cab as hot as an oven. The driver could sit in it no longer; he had to find some shade. He looked around. The landscape was completely flat; the only thing standing was a line of telegraph poles that ran parallel with the road. Even these did not create shade as the sun was directly overhead. The only place to hide from the sun's rays was under the truck. The driver crawled under there, and lying on his back on the hot tarmac he waited.

Eventually the rescue truck arrived. As the driver emerged from beneath his own vehicle he noticed that the telegraph poles now had shadows. These seemed to be equal in length to the height of the poles.

What time was it when help arrived?

see answer page 215

BUSY BEES

A colony of bees lives in a square-shaped beehive, the corners of which face north, south, east and west. The entrance to the beehive is on the south-facing corner. Bertie Bee is flying home, in a southerly direction, fully laden with pollen. On reaching his home he flies past the western corner at a distance of 2.5 m away and level with the entrance. Unable to negotiate a sharp left-hand turn, because of the weight he is carrying, he flies in a spiral around the hive and lands safely at the entrance. If the beehive is 50 cm^2 on each side, how far did Bertie fly from when he started his spiral to when he landed?

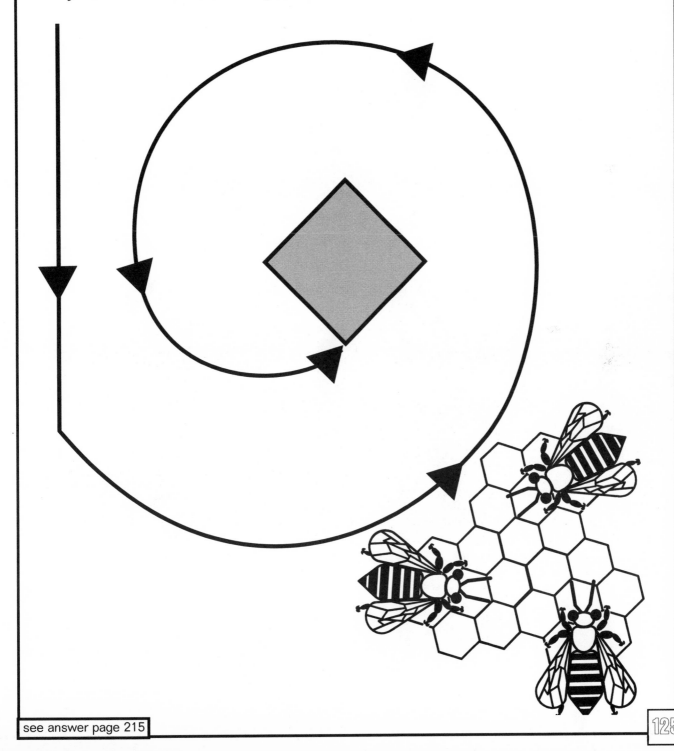

see answer page 215

A ROLL OF RIBBON

My wife has a small roll of white ribbon with which she wishes to decorate a present for a wedding. The ribbon is 0.01 cm thick and is wound around a center core 1 cm in diameter. The overall diameter of the roll is exactly 3 cm. Just before starting the decoration she asked, 'Can you tell me how much ribbon there is on this roll without me going to the trouble of unwinding it?'

'Of course my dear,' I replied, and set about the calculation.

How much ribbon was on the roll?

see answer page 215

A PACK OF CANDLES

A candle manufacturer needed to pack his candles in such a way as to prevent them moving about within the packaging and damaging each other. The best and cheapest packaging he could find was hexagonal tubing. Into cardboard tubing in the shape of a hexagon he could fit seven candles snugly, with six of the candles touching three others and the side of the tube, and the seventh candle held firmly by the other six. This method of packaging prevented movement and subsequent damage. If the candles are 3.5 cm in diameter, what is the length of one of the sides of the hexagon?

see answer page 215

TO CATCH THE TRAIN

Mr Commuter lives in a apartment in the center of town, but works in London. He garages his car some distance away from his home and uses it each morning to drive to the station where he catches the train to London. The garage is en route to the station. Mr Commuter walks the distance at a speed of 8 km/h and then motors the rest of the way at a speed of 40 km/h. The normal journey time is 21 minutes.

One morning he is late and runs to the garage at 16 km/h and motors to the station at 60 km/h. He completes the journey in 11 1/2 minutes.

How far is it from Mr Commuter's home to the station?

see answer page 216

THE TRAVELERS

survey was recently carried out at a busy airport to find just where all those travelers had been to. Of those interviewed 55 said that in the past year they had been to Spain, 53 had been to France and 79 to Germany. 18 had been to Spain and France, 17 to Spain and Germany, and 25 to France and Germany. 10 travelers said they had visited all three countries.

How many people took part in the survey?

see answer page 216

THE PINE TREE

In a forest grew a pine tree. The magnificent tree grew tall and perfectly straight. Its height reached a full 25 m. All was quiet and peaceful in the forest. The wild flowers grew, and the rabbits and squirrels played on the forest floor. The grass was speckled with sunlight, which peered through the branches of the pine tree. Slowly the sunlight was blocked by heavy rain clouds which blackened the sky, filling the forest with darkness. The small animals scurried back into the holes for protection. A storm was brewing.

Suddenly, and without warning, the forest was lit by a bolt of lightning. It struck the pine tree at a point some way up the trunk. The pine tree swayed as smoke rose from the wound. It swayed once more before it came crashing down, the noise almost drowned by the crash of thunder that followed the lightning bolt. The tree-top hit the forest floor some 5 m away from its base. The ground shook slightly with the impact.

As quickly as they had come the storm clouds cleared, and once again the sunlight beckoned the creatures out of their hiding places. They looked at the poor tree, standing with the fallen top part still attached to the trunk like some giant triangular monument, a lasting reminder of the power of nature.

How far up the trunk did the lightning strike?

see answer page 216

SINKING A WELL

Calculating the cost of sinking a well is quite a complicated procedure. The cost is directly proportional to the time it takes to sink the well. The time taken varies, as the depth varies, in two different ways: partly as the square of the depth and partly as the cube of the depth.

A well needs to be sunk to a depth of 20 m. The cost has been estimated at $50 per hour. The manager of the drilling rig knows that it took 60 hours to sink a well which was 10 m deep, and it took 146 1/4 hours to sink a well 15 m deep. He now needs to calculate the cost of sinking the new well 20 m deep.

Can you help?

see answer page 216

FIND THE FRACTION

With the popularity of the pocket calculator, standard fractions are becoming used less and less. This next little conundrum will help to exercise those skills that are in danger of being forgotten.

If seven is added to both the numerator and the denominator of a fraction, it becomes equal to 5/6. If instead five is added to the numerator and seven to the denominator, it becomes equal to 3/4.

Find the original fraction.

see answer page 216

THE BOWLING GREEN

The members of the local bowling club hold a meeting to discuss the condition of the green. In recent times the green has been ruined by local children playing on it when the club is closed. It is proposed that a trench be dug all around the green to try to prevent children gaining access and the soil from the trench be used to raise the surface of the green by 1 ft in height. The green is 300 ft long and 200 ft wide, and it is agreed that the trench needs to be 8 ft in width to prevent easy access.

How deep does the trench need to be to provide the necessary amount of soil?

see answer page 216

The Babylonians, who lived some 4,000 years ago, were the occupants of the area of land between the Tigris and Euphrates rivers, a land known as Mesopotamia. The ancient people of Babylon were quite remarkable. They had mastered the rudiments of algebra, and the relationship between the sides of a right-angled triangle was known to them many hundreds of years before it was attributed to Pythagoras.

An old Babylonian tablet unearthed at Susa asks for the radius of a circle circumscribing a triangle whose sides are 50, 50 and 60. Now these people did not, as far as we know, have access to tables of trigonomical values such as sine, cosine and tangents. They were able to solve the problem by use of algebra and the relationship between the sides of triangles.

Can you solve the problem without resorting to the use of trigonometry?

see answer page 217

DE MORGAN'S CONUNDRUM

Augustus De Morgan, an eminent mathematician of the 19th century, helped to found the British Association for the Advancement of Science in 1831. De Morgan was appointed a professor of mathematics at the newly established London University at the age of 22, where he continued to teach for many more years. He was a lover of conundrums, many of which are listed in his *Budget of Paradoxes* edited by his widow after his death.

At one time he proposed the following conundrum concerning his age: 'I was x years old in the year x squared.'

Can you figure out in what year Augustus De Morgan was born?

see answer page 217

A SQUARE IN A TRIANGLE

In the garden of a stately home, there is a pathway that forms an isosceles triangle. It surrounds three triangular flower beds and a square of lawn. The pathway measures 12 m by 10 m by 10 m. The lawn forms a perfect square and touches the pathway along the 12 m length. It also touches the two 10 m lengths of path at two points.

What is the length of the side of the lawn?

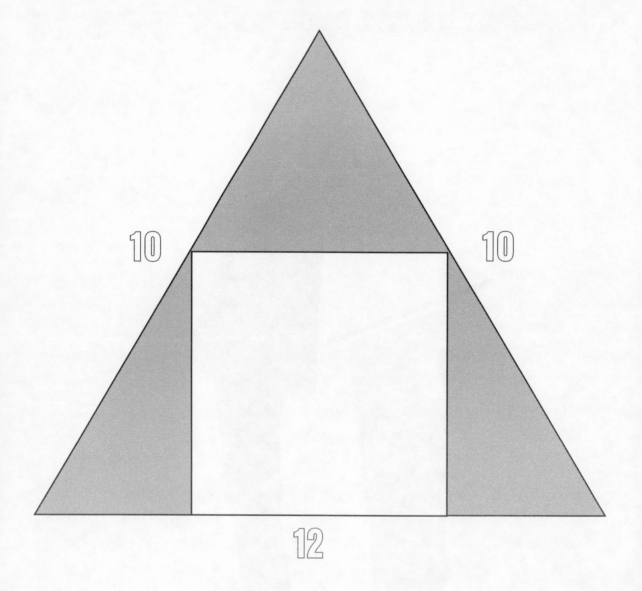

see answer page 217

BURIED TREASURE

Many years ago a group of six pirates uncovered a hoard of gold coins buried in the sand on a remote desert island. The captain of the group, being a mean and bloodthirsty cut-throat, demanded a third share of the booty for himself. No one argued except the first mate, who claimed that if the captain had a third share then the mate should have a quarter and the boatswain a fifth. The captain agreed but said that because the cook had to be kept sweet he could have an eighth share.

'What about us?' cried the last two pirates, one a scurvy crewman and the other the cabin boy.

'Here,' cried the captain, throwing 10 gold coins at the crewman, 'and as for little Jim here, he can have a single gold piece.' He passed the coin to the cabin boy and grinned a toothless grin, his foul breath choking the lad as he pressed it into his small soft hand.

'But . . .' stuttered the frightened cabin boy, 'how many coins have we found?'

see answer page 217

THE FARMER'S FIELDS

A farmer owns two plots of land. They are both perfectly square and together cover an area of 1,000 m^2. The length of the side of the smaller field is 10 m less than 2/3 the length of the side of the other field.

What are the dimensions of the two fields?

see answer page 217

Six men together win $180 at the races. The winnings are to be divided between them, but not in equal proportions. The sum is divided in such a way as to ensure the difference between the amounts is always constant, and the sum of the four largest shares is $5\frac{3}{7}$ times the sum of the two smaller shares.

How much did each man receive?

WASHING THE BLANKET

One day Mrs D. Tergent decides to wash her favorite blanket. Placing it in the washing machine and setting the program on hot wash, she stands back and watches as the machine does its job.

On completion of the wash Mrs D. Tergent starts to remove the blanket from the machine and stares in horror. It has shrunk. The blanket is now 7/8 of its original length and 9/10 of the original width.

By what percentage of its original area has the blanket decreased in size?

see answer page 218

STACKING THE SHELVES

A supermarket manager was designing a new display for breakfast cereals. He wished to display four different types of cereal in the ratio of 1:2:3:4. The display shelf held 10 packets less than his minimum requirements so he increased the length of the shelf by 50 per cent. The new shelf held all he required plus another 10 packets. Assuming all the packets were of equal thickness, how many of each type of cereal did he finally have on display when the new shelf was full?

see answer page 218

THE THREE DRUNKS

Fred, Stan and Bill foolishly embark on a drinking campaign to see just how much beer each one of them can consume before passing out. The rules are that each man will drink as much as he can and continue drinking until every one of them is completely paralytic.

Bill is the first to collapse in a drunken stupor, much to the amusement of the other two. Four pints later Stan follows him under the table, but Fred carries on drinking. Fred manages to force down yet another four pints before he can no longer stand upright. The landlord reckons that together they drank 15 liters of beer.

How many pints of beer did each man consume?

see answer page 218

A CUBIC CALENDAR

Two perfect cubes have numbers painted on the sides to enable them to be used as a calendar. By arranging the cubes, placed side by side, the number combination of the two faces on display can be made to show the date of each day in the month. There are 12 faces in total and each face has only one number painted on it.

What are the numbers on each face of the two cubes?

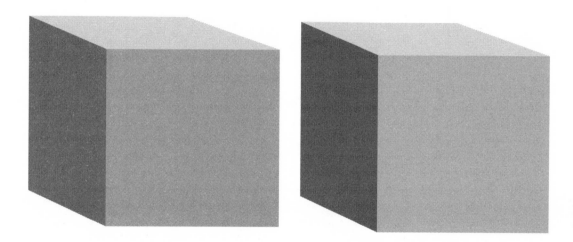

A FIVE-LETTER WORD

There is a five-letter word that contains three consonants and two vowels. Although the word has five letters, three of them are the same. The two vowels are different letters, but the three consonants are all alike.

What is the word?

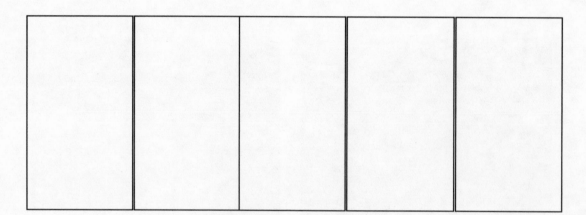

see answer page 218

AN ANGLE IN TIME

The old long-case clock in the corner of the room ticks away as it has done for over a hundred years. Time and constant cleaning has removed all the numbers and decoration from the clock face. Now all that is left are the hour and minute hands slowly revolving across a white background.

As I look at the clock it is a quarter past the hour, and the angle between the center lines of the hour and minute hands is 37.5°. In 20 minutes' time I will look at the clock again and find the angle between the two hands has changed to 72.5°. My stomach tells me it must be about time to eat.

Will someone please tell me what the time is now?

see answer page 218

FROM AN ELLIPSE TO A CIRCLE

If a circular cylinder is cut by an inclined plane that does not intersect the base, the resultant shape is an ellipse. It must follow from this that if an elliptical cylinder is cut by an inclined plane that does not intersect the base, it can form either another ellipse; or, if it is cut in the correct plane at the correct angle, the result can be a perfect circle.

An elliptical cylinder whose major axis is twice its minor axis is cut by an inclined plane with the resulting shape being a perfect circle.

At what angle and in what plane must this cut be made to give the desired result?

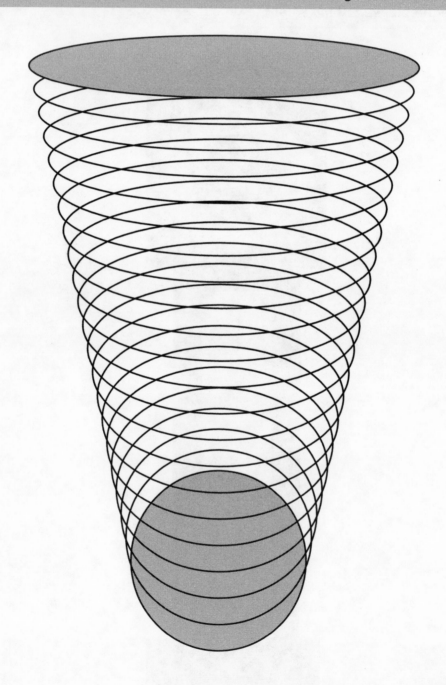

see answer page 218

On a Saturday morning in the market place there are many bargains to be had, particularly among perishable goods. On one particular day a flower-seller had a large amount of stock left that had to be sold. At 3 p.m. he offered flowers at a price of 10 for $4. By 3.30 he had increased the offer to 17 for $5. He continued to increase the offer during the afternoon until by close of trading he was practically giving them away at 39 for $7.

How many flowers did he offer for sale at the price of $6?

At the rear of Mr Mason's house there was a rectangular patio made from flagstones each 2 ft x 2 ft. The patio fitted nicely across the rear of his lounge on the north side and the wall of his extension on the west. Mrs Mason wanted the patio made smaller in order to create a flower bed. It was decided that the best way to do this was to cut along the diagonal of the patio from the south-west corner to the northeast corner with a stone saw and take up half of the flagstones leaving a triangular patio. Mr Mason could then use the uncut flagstones that he had removed to build a sun terrace at the bottom of the garden.

If the original patio measured 26 ft on the north side and 22 ft on the west, how many uncut flagstones did Mr Mason recover from the alteration?

see answer page 218

COWBOY JOE

Out riding one day Cowboy Joe finds himself 6 miles north and 2 miles west of his log cabin. He wishes to water his horse before starting the journey home. There is a long straight river 5 miles west of his present position which runs directly north to south.

What is the shortest route he can take to reach the river and then his home, and how far will he have to travel?

see answer page 219

THE POOL PLAYER

Aplayer wishes to hit the white ball so that it bounces off the cushion (assumed perfectly elastic) and strikes the other ball without first hitting the black.

Which of the positions marked on the cushion should the pool player hit the white ball towards to ensure hitting the red?

see answer page 219

Study carefully the diagram below. You will see a rectangle measuring 11 cm by 13 cm which has been divided into two parts by a diagonal line. Each section has been sub-divided into two triangles and a rectangle. But there is a problem. If you calculate the areas of the sub-sections on one side of the diagonal line and compare them with the areas of the other side you will find one side of the diagonal is 1 cm^2 larger in area than the other. Why?

What is wrong with the diagram?

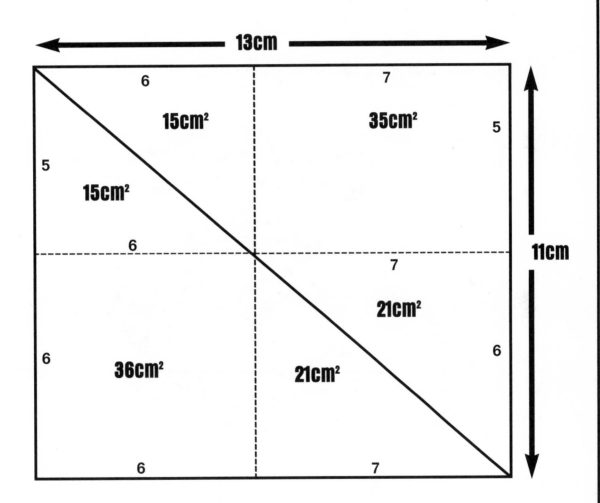

THE DRIPPING TAP

On my many business trips away from home I often find it difficult to sleep in a strange hotel bed. On one such occasion, lying awake in the early hours, I became aware of the sound of a tap dripping in the en suite bathroom. The sound appeared to become louder and louder in the silence of the room until it became almost deafening. All my attempts to stop the tap dripping failed. Even plugging my ears with cotton wool failed to stop the endless drumming of the drops of water hitting the base of the shower. It was then that I decided to count the drips to see if it would have the same effect as counting sheep and eventually send me to sleep. It didn't. The only good thing that came out of that unpleasant experience was this puzzle.

I started counting at 3.36 a.m. and my alarm clock was set to ring at 7.00 a.m. If the tap dripped at a rate of once every 17 seconds and I did not sleep at all that night,

How many drips did I count before the alarm went off?

see answer page 219

A regular polyhedron that has 20 faces is called an icosahedron. This is the largest number of faces that can be formed on a regular polyhedron. Each face forms the shape of an equilateral triangle, which means it will have 12 points or vertices. If an icosahedron has 20 faces and 12 vertices,

How many edges does it have?

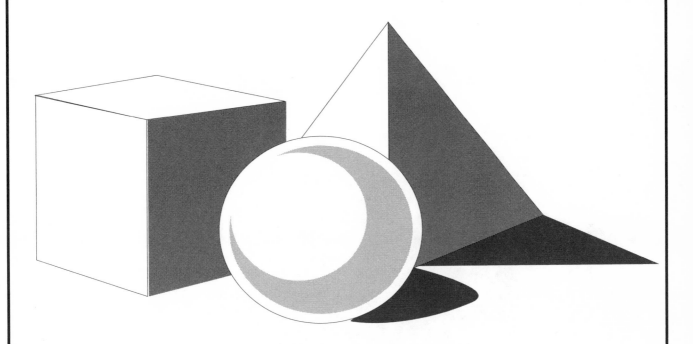

THE KINGDOM OF TRUTH

A long time ago in a far distant land there lived a king who decreed that it was a crime to tell a lie – a crime so serious that it was punishable by death. He discovered that one of his wives had been telling untruths for a long time, and she had to be put on trial, if only to prove to his subjects that no one was above the law. The court found her guilty as charged, but it was left to the king to sentence her.

Not wanting to see his wife killed, the king spoke privately with her before he passed sentence in open court. The court assembled to hear sentence passed.

The king said, 'You have been found guilty by this court, and the sentence is death, but you must say one last thing before you die. If your last statement is true, you will be given poison and you will die painlessly, but if your statement is a lie, you will be burned alive.

What had the king told his wife to reply?

see answer page 219

MISSING NUMBER

If I subtract six from a particular number, the result is divisible by seven. If I subtract seven from it, the result is divisible by eight, and if I subtract eight from it, the result is divisible by nine. In fact, whatever number I subtract from it, the result is divisible by one more than the number I subtracted.

What is the number?

HOW OLD IS GRANDMA?

'How old are you, Grandma?' the young boy asked one day.

'Don't you know it's rude to ask a lady's age?' replied Grandma to the curious little boy.

'Sorry,' replied the boy, 'I didn't know, but I still want to know your age.'

'Well, see if you can solve this puzzle,' smiled the old lady. 'It may help you with your sums.'

The little boy listened as his grandma spoke.

'Next year,' said the old lady, 'I will be six times as old as I am now, less six times as old as I was 10 years ago.'

How old is Grandma?

see answer page 219

COME INTO MY PARLOR

'Come into my parlor,' said the spider to the fly.
'That's very kind of you,' replied the fly. 'I will take a break. All this flying around does tend to tire one so.'

Without further ado the fly walked into the spider's den. The spider quickly slammed and locked the door behind him. Suddenly there were spiders everywhere. They pounced on the fly, dragging him to the floor. He felt a sharp pain in his side, and his head began to spin as the poison from the spider's bite slowly reached his tiny brain. From that point on the fly offered no resistance. The spiders wrapped him in silk and carried him into the store cupboard.

Shortly, the fly regained consciousness and opened his eyes. He struggled, but there was no escape. Lying face down he looked through the gap under the store cupboard door. He could see the remains of many of his fellow creatures scattered around the floor of the kitchen. The spiders were walking over them, busy laying the table for their next meal. The fly counted 166 legs altogether and, counting both the spiders and the remains of the dead flies, 25 bodies.

How many spiders were in the kitchen?

see answer page 219

THE COWBOY PLUMBER

A miserly factory owner needed a length of pipe-work installed in his factory. The pipe was to be 3 in in diameter and 120 ft long. It was to be used to carry steam from the boiler house to a heating unit attached to the far end wall of the factory. Instead of using a qualified plumber the factory owner asked an inexperienced pipe-fitter to do the job. The steel pipe was to carry steam at 165° C. The pipe-fitter did the best job he could, sealing the joints and securing the pipe as tight and as close to the wall as possible. The job over, the steam was allowed into the pipe. Within seconds the pipe began to twist and bend as it ripped itself out of its mountings. He had forgotten to take the expansion of the length of pipe into consideration.

If the ambient temperature of the factory is 20° C, by how much will a 120 ft long steel pipe increase in length when the temperature is raised by 145° C? (N.B. the coefficient of expansion of steel is 0.000012.)

see answer page 220

THE SPEEDBOAT

A motor boat traveling at a constant speed is timed over a distance of 4 km and an average speed is calculated. The speed is then increased by 3 km per hour, and it is found that the journey time has decreased by four minutes over the same distance.

What was the original speed of the boat?

see answer page 220

CHANGING THE FRACTION

If the fraction 7/17 has the same number added to both the numerator and the denominator, the fraction is changed to 3/5.

What number is added?

see answer page 220

The difference between the squares of two consecutive numbers is 53.

What are the two numbers?

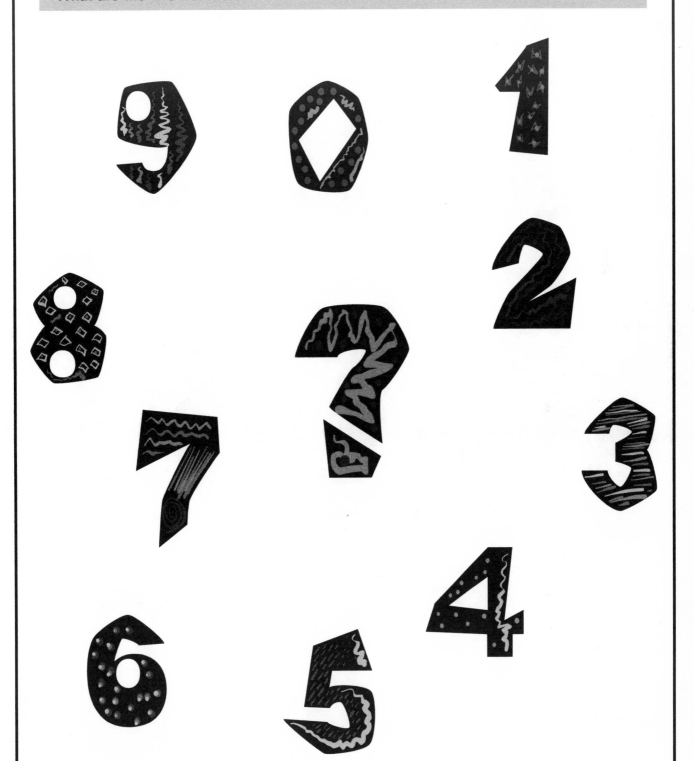

see answer page 220

In a simplified game of Bingo for children, there are 30 similar balls numbered one to 30 in a box. These are drawn out at random one by one and not replaced. Each child has a card with five numbers on it, and whenever a ball with one of those numbers is drawn out the child crosses off that number. The first child to cross off all five numbers on his card wins.

On this occasion there are only two children playing, Alan and Barry; Alan's card has the numbers 1, 8, 18, 19, 27 on it and Barry's has 1, 8, 10, 13, 29.

What is the probability that on the first draw neither Alan or Barry will cross off a number?

What is the probability that Alan will cross off a number on both the first and second draws?

On the first draw Alan crosses off a number but Barry doesn't.

What is the probability that this happens and that then on the second draw Barry crosses off a number but Alan doesn't?

see answer page 220

THE COST OF A CALL

Some years ago the cost of a telephone call was 1 cent for so many seconds. Later it was changed to 1 1/2 cents for six seconds more. As a result of the change the cost of a three-minute phone call was increased by 1 1/2 cents (a steeper price difference would accrue if the call was a second longer than three minutes).

How many seconds were we allowed for 1 cent before the change?

see answer page 220

THE SEATING ARRANGEMENT

The local amateur dramatic society is putting on its latest production. The audience can be seated partly in easy chairs and partly in upright chairs, for which the tickets will be cheaper. The hall has a floor area of 90 m^2; easy chairs require 1 m^2 of space, and upright chairs require 0.6 m^2. The organizers must allow for an audience of at least 100, but there are only 50 easy chairs available.

Assume that easy chairs are put in rows of 10 and tickets cost $4 each, upright chairs are put in rows of 12 and tickets cost $3.50 each, and the rows must alternate to maintain satisfactory sight lines to the stage.

Which layout will be the most profitable to the company, assuming all seats are sold?

see answer page 220

FROM THE MOUTHS OF BABES

As every parent knows, young children ask an enormous amount of questions – questions that show the inquisitiveness of a healthy young mind eager to learn. Sometimes the questions concern things we have never thought about before, things we have taken for granted and never questioned ourselves. These are the gems of learning, proof that things can be looked upon from a different angle, even by a young child. Here is one such typical conversation between a father and his small son.

'Dad, why do big balloons float up into the sky?'

'Because they are full of hot air and heat rises.'

'Do all hot things rise?'

'Heat makes anything that is fluid, such as gas or liquid, rise upwards.'

'So in a room the hottest place is next to the ceiling and the coldest place is next to the floor?'

'That's right.'

'So in the bath the hottest place is the top of the water, and the coldest place is on the bottom.'

'You've got it.' There then followed a short pause.

'Dad?' asked the boy after much deliberation.

'Is ice colder than water?'

'Yes, of course it is.'

'Why then does the fish pond freeze on the top and not on the bottom, if that is the coldest place?'

'Ask your mother.'

see answer page 220

PYTHAGORAS REVISITED

As all 15- and 16-year-old pupils studying for their mathematics exams will know, the Pythagorean theorem states that the area of the square drawn on the hypotenuse of a right-angled triangle is equal to the sum of the areas of the squares drawn on the other two sides.

This is the most proved theorem in mathematics and is all very well, but what about other shapes drawn on the sides of a right-angled triangle?

Is it true that the area of a regular pentagon drawn on the hypotenuse is equal to the sum of the areas of similar pentagons drawn on the other two sides?

see answer page 220

A GAME OF MARBLES

Six boys organize a marble competition between them. They start the game with 20 marbles each, and the competition is fierce. At the end of the game the winner has six times as many marbles as the boy who has lost the most. The other four boys have consecutive numbers of marbles left, and one of them has half as many as the winner.

How many marbles did the boy who lost the most have at the end of the game?

see answer page 220

A TALE OF TWO LADDERS

Two ladders, one 20 ft long and one 30 ft long, are placed against opposite walls of an alley, which is 11 ft wide. The foot of each ladder is placed firmly against the base of the wall opposite. The two ladders cross each other a certain vertical distance from the ground.

How far above the ground do the two ladders cross?

see answer page 220

THE THREE-NUMBER PROBLEM

I have chosen three numbers. The second is twice the first, and the third is three times the second. The sum of the first two when multiplied by the sum of the last two happens to be the same as the first number multiplied by the square of the second number.

What are the three numbers?

see answer page 220

THE GENIUS OF HIPPARCHUS

In the second century B.C. Hipparchus, the greatest astronomer of the ancient worlds, created a branch of mathematics that was ingeniously applied to the charting of the heavens and the earth. He had already instituted the system of locating points on the earth's surface by means of latitude and longitude, and he had calculated the radius of the earth by means of the ratios of the sides of a right-angled triangle – the method we now know as trigonometry. Hipparchus calculated the distance from the earth to the moon, or rather the distance from the center of the earth to the center of the moon.

How did he do it?

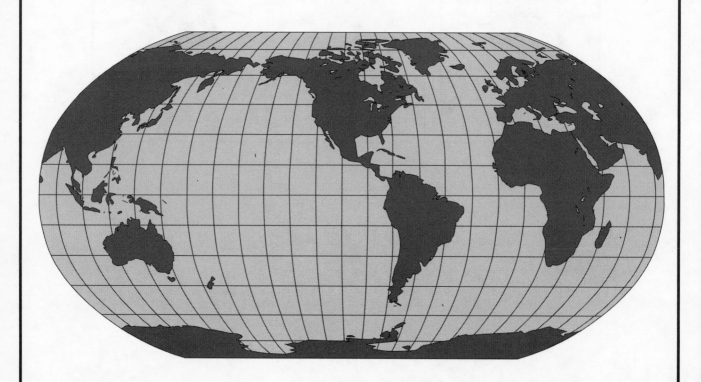

see answer page 220

WE ARE SAILING

Asailing ship is fitted with three sails of different sizes. When the largest sail is used, the ship can make a certain voyage in two days. When the next largest sail only is used, the voyage takes three days, and when the smallest sail only is used, the voyage takes four days.

How long will the voyage take when all three sails are used, assuming a constant wind speed?

see answer page 221

REDUCING THE CUBE

cube of a certain volume has its height reduced by 1/2. Its width is reduced by 2/3, but its length is trebled. The volume of the resultant cuboid is 864 cm^3.

What were the original lengths of the sides of the cube?

see answer page 221

DISKS IN A RECTANGLE

Two circular disks, one of radius 2 cm and the other unknown, can just be fitted into a rectangle whose sides are 6 cm and 5 cm. The two disks each touch two sides of the rectangle and the other disk.

What is the radius of the second disk?

PLANE FOR HIRE

A travel agency charted a plane for $1,200 to fly a party of people abroad. It was agreed that each member of the party should pay an equal share of the cost. It was later discovered that four members of the party would be unable to travel. The agency calculated that if it contributed $30, the fare of the remaining passengers would have to be increased by $5 in order to cover the cost of $1,200.

What was the original number of people in the party, and how much did each passenger finally pay?

see answer page 221

IN THE FOUNDRY

In a foundry a solid circular cylinder 7 cm long is to be melted down and reshaped into a solid rod 25 cm long. The cross-section of the rod is a regular hexagon whose sides are 2 cm.

What was the radius of the original cylinder?

After remolding, the rod is dipped into a protective fluid contained in a cylindrical tank of diameter 10 cm in such a way that the axes of the tank and the rod are both vertical.

If the rod is just immersed when it touches the bottom of the tank, what was the depth of the fluid before the rod was inserted?

see answer page 221

THE HIKERS

Three keen hikers, Brown, Smith and Jones, were out walking one day when they had a disagreement and decided to go on their separate ways. They were standing at the junction of two long straight roads which were inclined to each other at an angle of 60°. The three men leave the junction at the same time and walk at a constant speed of three miles an hour. Brown walks along the right hand fork and Jones along the left hand fork, while Smith walks across the fields between the two roads so that he is always an equal distance from each road. After walking for exactly an hour all three men stop, regretting the harsh words they have spoken to each other. They contact each other by mobile phone, and Smith suggests that he stays in his present position and the other two walk to where he is.

How far will Brown and Jones each have to walk to reach him?

Brown disagrees with the suggestion, turns around and walks back the way he came. After half an hour Jones, who is still at his original position, phones Brown and tells him to stay where he is and that he will walk to him by cutting across the fields.

How far will Jones now have to walk to reach Brown?

Jones contacts Smith and tells him he is going to walk to where Brown is now waiting and suggests Smith does the same. Smith, who realizes it is getting late and is tired of arguing, reluctantly agrees.

How far does Smith have to walk to meet up with the other two at Brown's position?

see answer page 221

A square sheet of metal whose sides measure 8 cm has two identical rectangles cut from the bottom left and the bottom right of the square. The removal of the rectangles produces a T-shaped piece with horizontal and vertical members which are the same width.

If the two rectangles that have been cut from the square are equal to half the original area, what is the width of the horizontal and vertical members of the T-shaped piece?

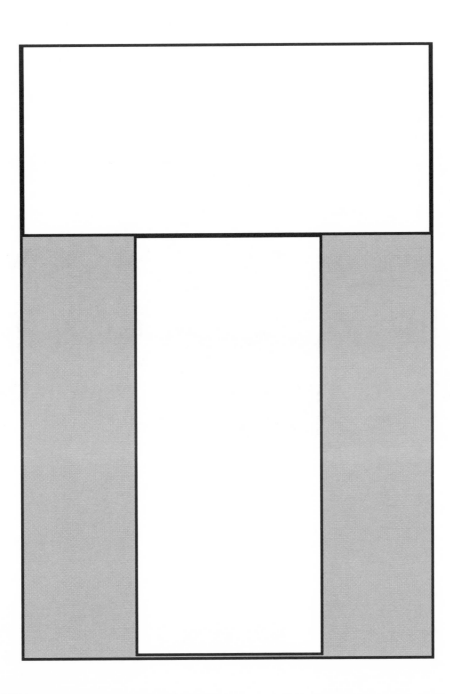

A large rectangular block of cheese whose edges measure 6 in, 4 in and 3 in is placed on a flat cheese board in the hotel dining room. In order to keep it fresh the head waiter places a large silver cover in the shape of a hemisphere over it. The cover rests on the cheese board and is such that the four top corners of the block of cheese are in contact with the inner surface of the hemisphere.

What is the radius of the inside of the hemisphere?

see answer page 222

FROM TOWN TO TOWN

A party of 11 people need to get to the next town, 40 miles away, as quickly as possible. The only transport available is a car, which can take a maximum of six people (including the driver) and can only travel at an average speed of 30 miles an hour. The 11 people set off at noon, six travelling by car and five walking at an average speed of 4 miles per hour.

The driver takes his passengers to the next town and immediately returns to meet the five walkers. He then takes them to meet with the original six at the next town. Ignore the time taken to set down and pick up passengers.

What time did the last five people reach the next town?

THE TETRAHEDRON

Four equilateral triangles, each of which has an area equal to the square root of 3 cm^2, are joined together to form a regular tetrahedron.

What is the volume of this tetrahedron?

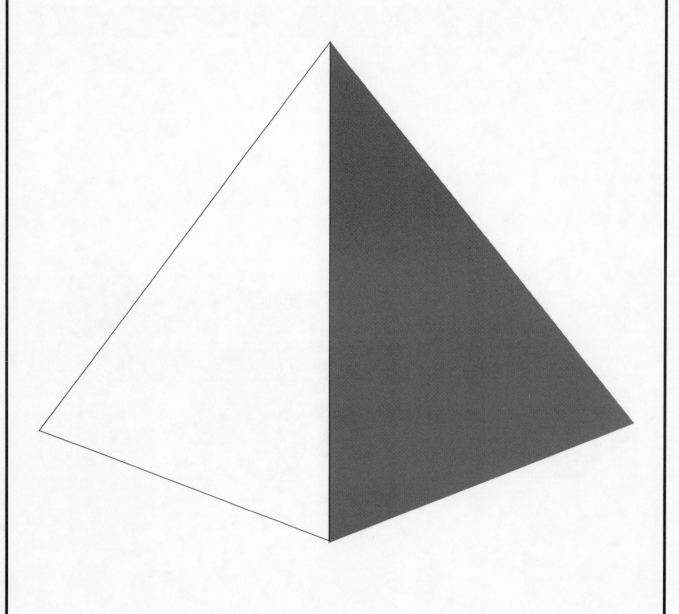

see answer page 222

THE SUM OF THE FRACTIONS

When a particular number is divided into quarters, thirds, fifths and eighths, I find that one-third plus one-eighth is one more than one-fifth plus one-fourth, but one-eighth plus one-fifth is 31 less than one-third plus one-fourth. Also one-fourth plus one-third plus one-fifth plus one-eighth is 11 less than the number itself.

What is the number?

see answer page 222

PERCENTAGE INCREASE

A farmer's produce is harvested and dispatched to the processing plant. The farmer, in order to stay in business, sells the produce for 15 per cent more than it costs him to grow it. The processing plant sells the goods to the wholesaler for 25 per cent more than it paid the farmer for them. The wholesaler adds 15 per cent to the price and sells them on to the retailer. The retailer, whose turnover is small in comparison, adds 50 per cent to the price he paid and then value-added-tax at 17.5 per cent. The shopper buys the goods for $1.75 per kilogram.

How much did it cost the farmer to produce them?

see answer page 222

A SIX-SHADED PROBLEM

If green plus blue makes 89, and red plus black makes 56,

What does yellow plus brown make?

see answer page 222

THE FUN RUN

Three unfit middle-aged men agree to test each other's fitness by competing in a charity fun run. The course is over rough country, and although the three set off full of energy and a keen competitive spirit, none of them manages to complete the course. Bill soon drops out, but Alan manages to run five times as far as him before he collapses with exhaustion. Charlie keeps going but gives up 1 km short of the finishing line.

If Charlie ran 3 km less than twice the distance Alan ran, and the three ran 21 km between them, how long was the course?

see answer page 222

MURDER AT THE MANOR HOUSE

Romeo and Juliet lived happily in the old manor house. They kept themselves to themselves and had no enemies as far as anyone knew. One day a hysterical maid ran to tell the butler that she had found them both dead on the living room floor. The butler went with the maid to the living room, and there, just as the maid had said, the bodies of the two were laying motionless on the floor. There was no sign of violence, and the bodies were unmarked. There was no evidence of forced entry, and nothing untoward except for some broken glass on the floor. The butler ruled out suicide, as they were not the type. Poison was also out of the question, as he had prepared and served their food himself. On examination of the bodies he could find no evidence as to the cause of death, but he did notice that the carpet on which they were lying was wet.

How did they die, and who killed them?

see answer page 223

THE COST OF SILVER PLATING

The cost of silver-plating a tray varies as the square of its length. If the cost of silver plating a tray 8 cm x 8 cm is $15,

What is the cost of plating a round tray 12 cm in diameter?

see answer page 223

THE DIET

Two foods, A and B, contain respectively 4 and 6 units of protein and 5 and 3 units of fiber. The cost of A is 40 cents per kilo, while B is 50 cents per kilo. The minimum daily intake is at least 16 units of protein and 11 units of fiber.

What is the cheapest way of meeting those requirements?

see answer page 223

THE SCHOOL CONCERT

At the school concert the price of the first three rows of chairs was $1 each, and the other seats cost 60 cents each. The takings were $204. On the second night of the concert the price of the fourth row of chairs was increased to $1, and the takings were $212.

Assuming the hall was full on both occasions and that there were the same number of chairs in each row, how many chairs were in the hall?

see answer page 223

INVESTMENTS IN SHARES

A man holds 200 shares in one company paying a dividend of 3 1/2 percent, the $1 shares in the company standing at $0.80. He also holds 400 shares in another company paying a dividend of 6 per cent whose $1 shares stand at $1.25. He sells both holdings and reinvests all the money in 5 per cent shares of nominal value $1 standing at $1.10.

What is his decrease in annual income?

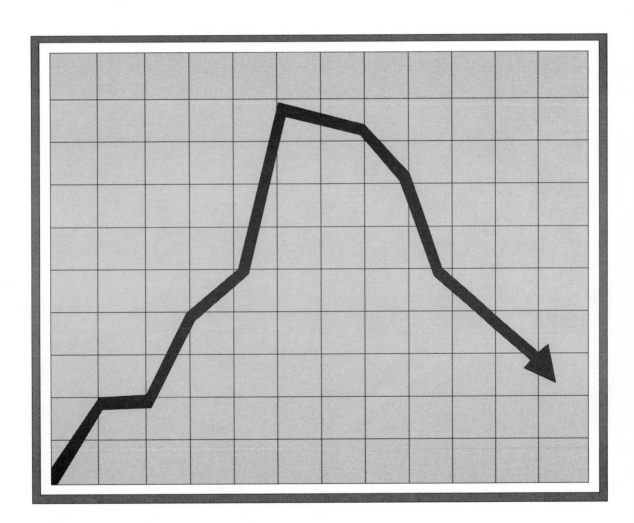

see answer page 223

ACROSS THE DESERT

The roads that cross the desert wastelands of the world are usually perfectly straight. On one such road there were four villages set at different distances apart. The third village was 60 miles from the first village; the fourth village was 40 miles from the second village, and the third village was 10 miles nearer to the fourth village than it was to the second village.

How far was it from the first village to the fourth village?

see answer page 223

A TALE OF TWO TREES

Two trees, an oak and an ash, grew together side by side in the forest. Over the years the ash grew to be 1 1/4 times as high as the oak. One day the woodcutter came along and lopped 3 m off the height of both trees. Now the ash is 1 1/3 times as high as the oak.

How high was the ash originally?

see answer page 223

BARRELS OF BEER

Two barrels of beer were both part full. One was 1/3 full and the other 9/14 full. If half the contents of the second barrel were emptied into the first and 2 1/2 liters were poured from the first barrel back into the second both would be half full.

How much would the barrels hold if they were both full?

see answer page 223

THE STRONGHOLD

Baron von Kinklehoffen built himself a castle to protect his ill-gotten gains from the hands of his enemies. He chose a flat piece of land high above the surrounding countryside on which to build it, and made every effort to make the building secure. The castle covered a section of land that was 50 yd on a side. His advisors told him that a good method of keeping out his enemies was to surround the castle with a moat. The baron agreed, and a moat was dug all the way around the outer walls of the castle.

Now the baron had to pay taxes based on the total area of land that the castle and moat occupied. When the final demand for his tax payment arrived, the baron studied it carefully. To his surprise he found that the area of land taken up by the moat was only 100 yd^2 less than the area of land on which the castle stood.

How wide was the moat?

see answer page 223

THE SWIMMER

Aboy wishes to swim across a river that is flowing at a rate of 1 m every five seconds. He wishes to land on the opposite bank 10 m below the point at which he enters the water. The river is 50 m wide, and he can swim at a speed of 0.5 m per second.

At what angle to the bank should he head, and how long will it take him to swim across?

see answer page 223

GOING SHOPPING

rs Spendalot likes to go shopping and also likes to exercise. She combines the two several times a week by walking to the shops, which are some distance from her home. The trouble with this arrangement is that Mrs Spendalot usually buys more goods than she can carry home and has to phone her husband to ask him to collect her in the car. Now, Mrs Spendalot walks at a speed of 5 km per hour, and her husband drives at an average speed of 30 km per hour. On a particular day Mrs Spendalot leaves home at 10 a.m., walks to the shops and spends two hours shopping. Phoning and waiting for her husband to bring the car takes a further 20 minutes, and she arrives back home at 12.55 p.m.

How far are the shops from her home?

see answer page 223

THREE FAT LADIES

Once upon a time there were three sisters who lived together at Corpulent Lodge in the village of Blubberville, set in the countryside of Tubbyshire. The three sisters, Annie, Betty and Cally, were what one might call large ladies. Their total weight was 900 lb. Annie was the largest of the three, weighing twice as much as Betty, while Cally was only 100 lb heavier than Betty.

What was the weight of each of the three sisters?

see answer page 224

CHANGING DIMENSIONS

Mr Hedges the gardener was building a vegetable garden. He selected a site which covered an area of 288 m^2 .He found that if he increased the length by 6 m and decreased the width by 4 m the area was unchanged.

What was the length and width of the original piece of land?

see answer page 224

THE FARMER'S DAUGHTERS

Farmer Giles had three daughters of whom he was very proud. He was surprised at how quickly they were growing up. Time was passing faster than he had expected, and already the eldest was talking about leaving home. This he strongly objected to until his wife made him realize that this time next year the eldest daughter would be one and a half times the age of the middle daughter, and the middle daughter would be twice as old as the youngest.

If the sum of their ages is now 33 years, what are the ages of the three girls?

see answer page 224

THE RAMBLERS

Agroup of keen walkers set off one day to climb a steep hill. They parked their car at the foot of the hill and began the four-mile journey to the summit. The hill was rocky, and the going was slow. It took them exactly two hours and 20 minutes to reach the top, including a 20-minute break half-way up. They rested at the summit for an hour, enjoying the view and their packed lunches, before setting off back. The downhill journey was much easier, and they ran most of the way down. They arrived back at their starting point feeling tired but happy that they had achieved their objective. The round trip had taken them exactly four hours.

Having covered a total of eight miles in four hours, the ramblers calculated that their average speed for the total journey was 2 mph.

But what was their average walking speed?

see answer page 224

DIRTY POOL

As most people know, pool consists of 15 colored balls and one white ball. At the start of the game, the colored balls are arranged in a triangular formation with the black ball at the center of the arrangement. The balls are placed in a triangular frame and positioned near the bottom center of the table, and the frame is then removed.

This next conundrum does not concentrate on the game of pool or even the balls but on the triangular frame. If, on this particular table, the balls are each 2 in in diameter, and 15 balls fit exactly into the frame,

What is the area of the triangle into which the balls are placed?

see answer page 224

THE BALLAD OF SHAMUS MAGEE

One day in the Forest of Dee
Crept a hunter named Shamus Magee
With his trusty arrow
Aimed strait at a sparrow
Way up at the top of a tree.

Now a sparrow is not a fierce prey,
Just not worth the time, some would say,
But the man in our ballad
Said, ''twill go well with a salad,'
And was the first game he'd spotted all day.

As Shamus now pulled back his bow,
He imagined the sparrow was crow;
He let loose the dart,
Aimed straight at the heart
Of the poor bird now fully on show.

At an angle of sixty degrees
The arrow flew into the trees.
Fifty meters per second
Was its speed, Shamus reckoned,
Unaided by wind or by breeze.

But the arrow flew harmlessly past
The bird perched high up on that mast.
With a chirping of fright
The sparrow took flight.
The word Shamus uttered was 'blast'.

In no time the sparrow had flown,
And Shamus was left there alone.
He now had to seek
For that arrow so sleek,
For it fell where the brambles had grown.

The arrow had made a full arc
And landed somewhere in the park.
It marked the ground
With a dull thumping sound,
But how far from our man was that mark?

see answer page 224

8.

1) 42. The interval between each term is a prime number in sequence.

2) 95. The interval between the terms is a square number in sequence.

3). The answer is 57. The interval between each term is a triangular number in sequence.

4) Each term = $N \times N^2$ where $N = 1, 2, 3, 4, 5, 6$; hence the last term is $7 \times 2^7 = 896$.

5) The numbers are 1/2, 3/4, 5/6, 7/8, 9/10 and 11/12 when written in decimals; therefore the last term is 13/14, which is 0.9268.

6) The answer is 1,458. Each term is three times the last.

7) The missing numbers are 21 and 567, each number being three times the last.

8) The numbers are 1 x 2, 3 x 4, 5 x 6, 7 x 8, 9 x 10, 11 x 12, so the next number in the series must be 13 x 14 = 182.

9) The terms in the series are (1), (2 + 3), (4 + 5 + 6), (7 + 8 + 9 + 10), (11 + 12 + 13 + 14 + 15) and (16 + 17 + 18 + 19 + 20 + 21), so the missing term is (22 + 23 + 24 + 25 + 26 + 27 + 28), which equals 175.

10) The interval between each term is double the interval between the previous two terms, so the last number in this series is 127.

9.   The Four Jays

The little clue 'June is in her prime' should have helped, as it suggests that all the numbers in her name are prime numbers. As the total is 17 all the numbers must be less than 10, so:

J = 2
U = 7
N = 5
E = 3

Setting these numbers in the word Jane or Jean we can conclude that 16 = 2 + A + 5 + 3 so A = 6.

Putting these numbers in the word Jenny in the same way we find Y = 4.

10   The Woodcutter's Conundrum

Referring to the diagram we see we have a right-angled triangle with R as the hypotenuse, (R - 1) the second side and 5 cm the third side. Now:

$R^2 = (R - 1)^2 + 5^2$

So $R^2 = R^2 + 2R + 1 + 25$

$0 = 2R + 1 + 25$

$2R = 26$. So $R = 13$. Hence the radius of the curved section is 13 cm.

11.   The Farmer's Fields

The first piece of land measured 63 m by 64 m and the second 252 m by 2 m giving areas of 4,032 m^2 and 504 m^2 respectively. Therefore the total length of fencing he needed to buy was:

2(63 + 64) + 2 (252 + 2) = 254 + 508 = 762 m.

12.   Three Little Boys

The first boy had 16 five-cent coins; the second had 11 ten-cent coins; and the third had seven fifty-cent coins.

13.   Letters to Numbers

A = 9, B = 8, C = 7, D = 6, E = 5, F = 4, G = 3, H = 2, I = 1, J = 0, and the operation is multiplication so:

CAB = CGHGF becomes 7 x 9 x 8 = 7 x 3 x 2 x 3 x 4

DAB = HGGGFH becomes 6 x 9 x 8 = 2 x 3 x 3 x 3 x 4 x 2

GIB = GB becomes 3 x 1 x 7 = 3 x 7

CACH = GCCD becomes 7 x 9 x 7 x 2 = 3 x 7 x 7 x 6

14.   The Engineer

The engineer formed the cavities by using expanded polystyrene blocks suspended from the metal reinforcing with wire and accurately positioned. The concrete was gently poured around them and allowed to set. When the concrete was partly cured a solvent was poured onto the polystyrene which dissolved it totally. As concrete does not fully cure for 28 days, there was enough time for the solvent to evaporate and not to interfere with the chemicals in the compound. All that was left in the cavities was a sticky residue which lay harmlessly at the bottom of the pocket.

15.   Training the Trainee Train Driver

On the diagram, each number represents a position on the track. First move the engine down and connect to carriage B. Now move carriage B and leave it at position 3. Move down the track and connect to carriage A. Change the switches, move this carriage a short way back up the track and leave it at position 4. Let the engine travel all the way around the track, passing through the tunnel and re-connecting to carriage B. Back up a short way and change the switches again so that we can move both engine and carriage B to re-connect to carriage A. Now move the engine and both carriages around to position 2. Disconnect the engine and travel all the way around the track so that the engine arrives at the other side of the two carriages. Push both carriages into the siding and disconnect carriage B at position 5. Move back down the track and disconnect carriage A at position 1. Leaving carriage A in its new position we can now travel all the way around through the tunnel once again to arrive back at the other side of carriage A.

Reverse up the siding and re-connect to carriage B. Reverse down the siding, and move carriage B around to its new location at position 1. Now drive the engine back to its original position 5.

16.   Serving the Wine

The manager has two identical glass jugs and two containers, one holding three units and the other five.

| 0 | 0 | 3 | 5 |

First he empties the three units into one of the glass jugs.

| 0 | 3 | 0 | 5 |

He then fills the three-unit container from the fiveunit container,

| 0 | 3 | 3 | 2 |

putting the two units remaining into the empty jug.

| 2 | 3 | 3 | 0 |

He then pours the three units into the five

| 2 | 3 | 0 | 3 |

and tops up the five from the first jug.

| 2 | 1 | 0 | 5 |

Now he again fills the three unit container from the five.

| 2 | 1 | 3 | 2 |

Placing the two jugs together he pours wine from the three units into the jug holding one unit until the levels of the two jugs are the same,

| 2 | 2 | 2 | 2 |

leaving two units in each of the jugs and the containers.

17.   Little Tommy Tomkins

Little Tommy Tomkins explained that he had been measuring time from the family's 12-hour clock, so he insisted quite correctly that all the additions were accurate:

7 o'clock plus 10 hours is 5 o'clock.
8 o'clock plus 17 hours is 1 o'clock.
4 o'clock plus 11 hours is 3 o'clock.
9 o'clock plus 7 hours is 4 o'clock.
6 o'clock plus 8 hours is 2 o'clock.
5 o'clock plus 7 hours is 12 o'clock.
The teacher had to agree.

18. Get It Out!

The engineer would pack the center of the bearing as tightly as possible with thick grease. Then, after making sure that the grease did not hold any air pockets, he would place a shaft of the correct size into the hole in the center of the bearing. He would then strike the shaft sharply with a soft hammer. The force of the hammer blow would be transmitted to the grease, which, with nowhere else to go, would be pushed into the small gap behind the bearing. The grease would transmit the pressure to the housing and to the bearing, which would move upward.

19. Chasing the Girls

The boys had found that their apartment numbers were the sum of the Roman numerals in their names:

Alex = L + X = 60

Phillip = I + L + L + I = 102

Using the same system they found that Diana would live at number 501:

D + I = 501. Thus the girl who lived at number 12 must have a name whose letters add up to that number. The only combinations they could find were:

X + I + I = 12   and   V + V + I + I = 12

Unable to think of a girl's name with an X and two I's in it, they convinced themselves her name must be Vivian.

20. More MPG

For the upward journey, at the rate of 10 miles to the gallon, Mr Stingy would use 1/10 of a gallon of fuel. The downward journey would use only 1/100 of a gallon, so the round trip would use 0.11 gallons . Average fuel usage is calculated by distance divided by consumption so 2 miles divided by 0.11 gives an average of 18.18 miles per gallon.

21. The Flight of the Pigeons

The answer to this conundrum is largely theoretical, but I believe that the overall weight of the vehicle and cargo would not change whether the birds were in flight or not. When a bird flies its weight is supported by the air beneath its wings. The air within the container is supported by the container, so the total weight of the cargo would be constant, the weight of the birds being transferred to the air and the combined weight being supported by the container.

22. The Klondike

Although there are infinitely many ways of solving his problem, the prospector chose the simplest and quickest: he knew that reducing a circle's circumference by half reduces its area by a quarter. By using half the rope he formed a circle 1/4 the size, so he formed two circles using the whole length of rope and in doing so retained half the original area. His claim formed a shape like a "figure 8", each circle being 140 yd in diameter and enclosing an area of 15,393.8 yd^2 or 3.18 acres.

23. Walking the Plank

The way to solve this kind of problem is to put the width over the length, multiply this by a constant 'K', and make it equal to the known weight. Then we need to find a value for K from this, and put it into a second equation using the new dimension. With all our measurements in the same units:

20/1,500 x K = 200

20K/1,500 = 200

20K = 300 000

K = 15,000

Using the value of K we can work out the weight the new plank will hold.

30/2,000 x 15,000 = 225, so the new plank will hold 225 kg.

24. Digital Crossword

There is probably more than one solution to this puzzle, but mine is shown below:

a. 6 + 2 + 18 = 26

b. 20 + 25 + 13 + 1 + 5 = 64

c. 25 + 4 + 8 = 37

d. 4 + 3 + 24 = 31

e. 8 + 7 = 15
f. 18 + 23 + 13 + 3 + 7 = 64
g. 23 + 22 + 10 = 55
h. 22 + 1 + 24 = 47
i. 17 + 10 + 5 = 32

25. Playing on the Swings

Make a sketch of the path of the swing, then form two right-angled triangles with a hypotenuse of 3.6 m and an adjacent side of 2.4 m. Find the angle which the swing passes through by using trigonometry.
Cos x = 2.4/3.6; x = 48.1896°, say 48.2°
Multiply this by two and we have the angle 96.4°. 96.4° divided by 360 will give us the fraction of the full circle that the swing traveled: 0.2677˙.
Now calculate the circumference of the full circle and multiply it by this number to find the length of the arc of the swing:
2 x 3.142 x 3.6 x 0.26777˙ = 6.057 m

26. The Infinite Stadium

Instead of moving the spectators as before, the manager moves the person in Seat 2 into Seat 3, the person in Seat 3 into Seat 5, the person in Seat 4 into Seat 7, and so on. The infinite number of seats with even numbers are now vacant for the infinite number of latecomers.

27. The Witch's Polyhedron

The crystal ball, with each face shaped like a pentagon, would have 12 sides, and is called a dodecahedron.

28. Numerical Code

This code needs the use of a nine-digit display pocket calculator. Type in the numbers 378163771 and read the display upside down. You should see the word ILLEGIBLE.

29. Noughts and Crosses (Tic–Tac–Toe)

By substituting the digit 1 for each X the lines of the matrix can be read as binary numbers. The lines have the value 5, 7 and 11. These are all prime numbers, so logically the next number in the array will have the value 13, which would be:
X   X   0   X

30. Stone-Throwing

The range of a projectile on a horizontal plane is found by squaring the velocity, multiplying it by the Sine of twice the angle and dividing by gravitational acceleration. This gives a distance of 91.83 m.

31. Musket Balls

The volume of a sphere is 4/3 multiplied by Pi (π, or 3.142) times the radius cubed. The volume of a cylinder is Pi times the radius squared multiplied by the height. If we express the height of the cylinder as:
$H = 3 \times 4/3\pi r^3$ divided by πr^2, we have the height equal to 4r, which is twice the diameter of the cylinder.

32. Missing Word

The answer to the eight clues are:
1. Defend
2. React
3. Repent
4. Depend
5. Acid
6. Agonize
7. Elope
8. Her
The three-letter word that can be added to the end of the first four words and to the beginning of the last four is ANT.

33. Numbers for Letters

The full analysis of the puzzle is as follows.
Taking Column 1 and Row 2, we have:
2P + S + Q = 102
SP + 2S = 90
Subtraction gives - S + Q = 12
so Q = S + 12
Taking Row 3 and Row 1 we have:
2R + Q +P = 143
R + Q + P + S = 119
Subtraction gives R - S = 24
So S = R - 24, therefore R = Q - 12

Taking Column 3 (substituting for S and Q):
2R + R - 24 + R - 12 = 136
4R - 36 = 136
4R = 160 so R = 43
Taking Row 3 and substituting for Q:
R - 12 + 2R + P = 143
3R - 12 + P = 143
3R + P = 155
P = 155 - 3R   but R = 43
P = 155 - 129 then P = 26
As S = R - 24 then S = 19
As Q = R - 12 then Q = 31

34.   Elementary Series

The clue was in the title. Each letter is the chemical symbol of an element written in the order of their atomic numbers.
B is boron, atomic number 5
C is carbon, atomic number 6
N is nitrogen, atomic number 7
O is oxygen, atomic number 8
F is fluorine, atomic number 9
So the missing letter(s) are Ne. Ne is neon, which has the atomic number 10.

35.   Changing Signs

There is only one way to arrange the signs to complete the sum:
$2 \div 3 - 4 + 5 \times 6 = 10$

36.   The Inaccessible Object

The surveyor measures the angle of elevation of the rock formation from two points 50 m apart. From this he can calculate the height by multiplying the distance between the two points by the product of the tangent of the two angles, and dividing by the difference between the tangents of the two angles:
Let the first angle be called angle A and the second angle B, the unknown distance to the rocks X and the height H, then:
H/X = Tan A and so X = H/Tan A
H/X + 50 = Tan B; H = Tan B (X + 50)
Substituting for X we have
H = Tan B ((H/tan A) + 50)
So H = (H tan B/Tan A) + 50 Tan B
It follows that H Tan A = H Tan B + 50 Tan B Tan A

So H Tan A - H Tan B = 50 Tan B Tan A
H(Tan A - Tan B) = 50 Tan B Tan A
Thus H = 50 Tan B Tan A/Tan A - Tan B

37.   Extra Letter

The quote is from 'The Farewell' by Charles Kingsley. From the bottom left, the words can be traced: 'Be good sweet maid and let who can be clever.' The letter H at the end is not part of the sentence.

38.   Triangles

The triangle is formed on the surface of a sphere. Imagine, if you can, two travellers standing exactly on the equator, one in Africa and the other in South America. Both men head north. Their direction of travel makes a 90° angle with the equator in each case. They will eventually meet at the north pole, making the third angle. The only triangles that have angles of 180° are those constructed on a flat surface.

39   You Can't Take It With You

The judge ordered the attorney to put all the money into a separate bank account. He was then to write a check for the full amount to Mrs Avarice, sign it, and place it in the coffin. The cremation would then go ahead as planned. If the check had not been cashed within 30 days, the money would be evenly divided between the immediate descendants.

40.   The Haunted Hotel

Take the room number where the sightings are at present, multiply that by number of days between the sightings, then subtract the number of days between the sightings. The number of days between sightings increases by one for each period, so room 3 x 2 - 2 = room 4; 4 x 3 - 3 = 9. So the next sighting is calculated by 9 x 4 - 4 = 32. The next room to be visited by the restless spirit would be Room 32, and the sightings would occur every fifth night.

41.   The Used Car

The answer is 26%.

42. The Shepherd and his Sheep
The structure would enclose the largest area if it was built 22 m wide and 46 m long, giving an area of 1,012 m^2.

43. The Gambler
The answer is $1,960.00

44. The Bus Driver
The answer is 32 five-cent pieces.

45. Touching Circles
The radii of the three circles are 5 cm, 4 cm and 1 cm.

46. The News Vendor
Since three people buy all three papers, 14 buy the Echo and the Moon, 12 buy the Moon and the Advertizer and 13 buy the Echo and the Advertizer. Since 70 buy the Echo, the number who buy the Echo only must be 70 - 14 - 13 - 3 = 40. 60 buy the Moon, so the number who buy the Moon only is 60 - 12 - 14 - 3 = 31. 50 buy the Advertizer, so the number who buy the Advertizer only is 50 - 12 - 13 - 3 = 22. Thus the newsagent has 40 + 14 + 31 + 12 + 3 + 13 + 22 customers, that is 135.

47. Weather Changes
The probability that it will be fine on Sunday is found by working out the total number of combinations of weather changes for the next three days. They are:
Fine, fine, fine.
Wet, fine, fine.
Fine, wet, fine.
Wet, wet, fine.
The probability for each combination and add them together:
3/4 x 3/4 x 3/4 +1/4 x 1/3 x 3/4 + 3/4 x 1/4 x 1/3 + 1/4 x 2/3 x 1/3, which equals 347/576 – so I think I'll risk walking on Sunday.

48. The Sum of the Parts
Let the length of the table = L, the area = A and the cost = C, so C = aA + bL^2

When A = 6 and L = 3, C = 50,
so 50 = 6a + 9b
When A = 6 and L = 4, C = 64.
so 64 = 6a + 16b
Subtraction gives 14 = 7b so b = 2
Substitution gives 50 = 6a + 18 so a = 5 1/3
Therefore the connection between C, A and L is C = 5 1/3A + 2L^2
When A = 6.25 and L = 2.5
C = (5 1/3 x 6.25. + (2 x 6.25)
The cost of a table 2.5 m square is $45.83.

49. One Man and his Dog
The best way to solve this puzzle is to forget about the dog for a moment and concentrate on the farmer. If the farmer walks at a constant speed of two miles per hour for a journey of three miles, then the walk will take him 1 1/2 hours. Assuming the dog runs constantly for that period of time at a speed of six miles per hour, the dog will cover a total distance of nine miles.

50. The Prince and the Princess
The prince knew that the princess was highly intelligent and would instinctively know what part she had to play in the plan. First he bought a casket and a padlock. He then wrote a letter, placed it in the casket, and sealed it with the padlock. The guard took the casket to the princess. On receiving the casket the princess fastened a padlock of her own onto the casket and told the guard to return it to the prince with both padlocks intact. When the casket reached the prince he removed his own padlock and told the guard to take it back to the princess. She then removed her padlock, opened the casket and read the letter. This mode of communication continued until the war was over.

51. Chickens and Ducks
The maximum number of eggs per week, given the constraints of an $80 investment

and a maximum number of 25 birds, will come from 16 chickens and eight ducks:
16 + 8 = 24 birds
16 x $4 + 8 x $2 = $80 investment
16 x 5 + 8 x 4 = 112 eggs per week.

52. The Open Box Question
The box would measure 53.4 cm by 53.4 cm by 13.3 cm and would have a volume of 37,925.7 cm^3.

53. The Car Park
The maximum number of vehicles that the car park could hold is 350: 300 cars and 50 trucks. To maximize revenue, the car park would provide spaces for 200 cars and trucks, giving an hourly income $900 .

54. The Tiler's Dilemma
The larger of the two tiles would be 8 cm square and the smaller 6 cm square.

55. The Lost Consonants
The quotation is from Shakespeare's *Twelfth Night* I,i: IF MUSIC BE THE FOOD OF LOVE, PLAY ON.

56. A Pile of Bricks
The smallest number, which when divided by two, three, four, five and six leaves remainder one but divides exactly by seven, is 301. There were 301 bricks in the original pile.

57. The Lion, the Donkey and the Carrots
The traveler would have to remove the carrots from the donkey's back and take the donkey across the river first. He would then return, take the lion across, then bring the donkey back with him. He would then leave the donkey and take the carrots across. Finally he would return for the donkey.

58. Counting Sheep
If 10 acres are sufficient to pasture 15 sheep for a period of 18 weeks, then proportionately 36 acres would be sufficient to pasture 54 sheep over the same period.

59. The Merciless Captain
The captain issues all crew members with a number and orders them to form a circle standing in single file in numerical order. He then counts in nines, starting with number one and throwing every ninth crew member into the sea. The Dognians are issued with the numbers 1, 2, 3, 4, 10, 11, 13, 14, 15, 17, 20, 21, 25, 28, 29. The unfortunate Catanians have the numbers 5, 6, 7, 8, 9, 12, 16, 18, 19, 22, 23, 24, 26, 27, 30.

60. Feeding the Needy
There are six possible solutions to this problem, seven if we include the one where there are no women in the village. The most popular answer is 11 men, 15 women and 74 children.

61. What, No Pi?
You may or may not know that the area of a circle can be found by multiplying the radius of the circle by the circumference and then dividing by two. In other words, the area of a circle is exactly the same as the area of a triangle whose base is the radius of the circle and whose height is the circumference.

62. Catch Me If You Can
The car would catch up with the bike after traveling for 34.07 minutes. The car travels at a speed of 50/60 km per minute, so 50/60 x 34.07 = 28.39 km. Thus Father catches John when he is 28.39 km away from home.

63. Slow Down George!
Poor old George had timed his journey exactly to try to prevent his nagging wife from complaining about having to visit at the terminal. His original speed would have been 84 km per hour, giving them a journey time of 1 hour 40 mins. Reducing his speed by 14 km per hour to 70 km per hour meant that the journey would take two hours, making them 20 minutes late.

64.   The Conference
The number of ways in which the members can be arranged in groups of three with the leader of each group always placed in the middle is 768.

65.   Connections
The word I'm thinking of is 'hypo', which means 'under,' 'below normal' or 'slightly'. It is also the nickname for sodium thiosulphate, a photographic fixer. Some of the 12 new words prefixed by 'hypo' are: hypochondria, hypocrisy, hypodermic, hypotenuse and hypoventilation. I'll leave you to find the rest.

66.   The Hockey Team
A mixed hockey team containing five men and six women chosen from seven men and nine women can be formed in 1,764 different ways, so the team would have to play that number of matches before all possible combinations had been tried.

67.   The Astronaut
The height above the surface of the earth, where the astronaut's weight would be 1/10 of that on earth is calculated by:
$$1/10 = 63702/d^2$$
That is, $d^2 = 10 \times 6,3702$
$d = \sqrt{10} \times 6,370$
$d = 20,143.7$ km
Therefore his height would be $20,143.7 - 6,370 = 13,773.7$ km

68.   Take A Hike
The answer is 24 miles.

69.   A Drive to the Med
Mr White had to buy an extra liter of oil, so we can take it that the $2.60 he spent over his estimated amount was the cost of this oil. He bought 3 liters of oil on the journey, so the amount spent on fuel was $87.60 less 3 x $2.60 = $79.80.
1,200 km at a rate of 9 km per liter would mean a total fuel usage of 1,200/9 - 133 1/3 liters. Cost per liter is found by Total cost/Total used, so $79.80/133 1/3 = $0.5985. So his average price per liter was $0.60.

70.   The Fish Pond
Mr Brown's calculations found the precise surface area of the pond's foundations; however, unless Mr Brown has some method of making a flat sheet into the exact shape of his pond – that is, an inverted top hat shape – then 22m^2 will be too small. If he lays the flat sheet over the site and then pushes the sheet into the hole, the sheet will inevitably fold over on to itself around the walls. This will take up the extra 6 m^2 of material. In reality, waterproof material is almost always sold from a roll. So Mr Brown would need material from a roll 6 m wide, and he would have to buy a length 6 m long. This means he would have to buy 36 m^2 in order to cover a precise area of only 22 m^2.

71.   The Prisoner.
The best method of solving this problem is by the use of quadratic equations, but to save you the trouble the walls are 0.676 m or 67.6 cm thick.

72.   The Airliner
The minimum number of economy-class passengers allowed under these conditions is 88.

73.   Hieroglyphics
Cover the right-hand half of each of the symbols: you'll see the numbers 1, 3, 5 and 7. The next symbol in the series will obviously be 9 – but it will appear as one number attached to a reversed 9.

74.   The Schoolteacher
The number of consecutive days is 15.

75.   Share and Share Alike
The price per loaf was $1.50.

76.   The Sheep Ranch
Lucky Mr Thrifty can expect to receive $83,026.73 from the sale of the land.

77.   Fuel Prices
Mr Thrifty used to spend $800 per year on fuel before the increase in price.

78.   Take the Train
Trains now run 1 1/3 times as fast.

79.   The Jogger
Poor Mr Smith could only manage to run 1.8 miles before he had to hail the taxi.

80.   In the Bar
The bartender was 36 years old. The customer's age was 40 years.

81.   Still in the Bar
If the total of the price of the bottle plus the top was 8 cents and the bottle cost 6 cents more than the top, then the top cost 1 cent to make.

82. Digits, Digits and More Digits
The three answers are 39, 78, and 973.

83.   Working His Way Through College
Ivor did not attend work for three days out of the 20 days he was employed.

84.   Student Life
The smaller of the two rooms that make up Ivor Nodosh's flat measures 12 ft x 12 ft, and the larger measures 13 ft x 13 ft.

85.   Think of a Number
The number I am left with after the calculations is 3.

86.   Think of a Number (Again)
There are four possible numbers: 21, 42, 63 and 84.

87.   Party Time
There were 100 cans of beer to share at the party.

88.   The Boatman
The speed of the current was a constant 2 mph. With the current the boat had an overall speed of 8 mph and against the current a speed of 4 mph, so the boatman's journey time would be doubled.

89.   The Round Trip
The distance between Southtown and Northtown is 48 km by train.

90.   Vacation by the Sea
Mr Mensaman had a vacation that lasted 15 days, but with a little more careful planning it could have lasted 20 days.

91. A Day in the Life of a Greengrocer
Mr B. Troot bought 300 pineapples and sold only 270 at 8 cents each profit. 300 pineapples for $72 means he paid 24 cents each for them. He sold 270 at 32 cents each, giving him $86.40 income. $86.40 less $72 gives a net profit of $14.40. He paid 20 cents per pound for the apples, and bought 80 sacks at $1.50 and 40 sacks at $1.70.

92.   More and More Moores
Old Mrs Moore had five children originally.

93.   Are You Sitting Comfortably?
The woman had been waiting 36 minutes.

94. Coffee Break Quiz
1. A stitch in time saves nine.
2. To be or not to be. (2B pencil)
3. Red sky at night, shepherd's delight.
4. One swallow does not make a summer.
5. Too many cooks spoil the broth.
Answers to the bond films:
1. Doctor No
2. Moonraker
3. Golden Eye
4. Octopussy
5. Thunderball
The tie-break answer is: 'The Charge of the Light Brigade'.

95. Take the Train 2

The two trains pass each other at 14:00, 75 km from Brotherton.

96. How High is the Mountain?

Draw a circle with a small bump on the top. Now draw a line from the top of the bump to the circumference. This line forms a tangent to the circle and hence meets a radius of the circle at 90°. Now draw a line from the center of the circle to the top of the bump, and we have a right-angled triangle. The angle between the two radii is the same as the angle of depression, so we can now calculate the lengths of the sides of the triangle by trigonometry. The radius of the circle (which represents the earth) is half the diameter = 3,957 miles. The distance from the center of the earth to the top of the mountain is found by 3,957/Cos 1.97 = 3,959.34. Subtract the radius of the earth from this figure and we have the height of the mountain. 3,959.34 - 3959 = 2.34 miles. Multiply this by 5,280 = 12,355 ft.

97. What Time is it Over There?

There are 24 hours in a day, and the earth is divided into 360°. If we convert the hours into minutes and divide by 360, we will find that for each degree of movement, east or west, there will be a time difference of four minutes. So 75° west will give an addition of 300 minutes to the time at Greenwich. If it is 12 noon at Greenwich, then it will be 17.00 hours at 75° west or 5 pm.

98. Over a Barrel

The barrel will hold 112.2 gallons. If you calculated the answer correctly without cheating, then there is only one thing I can say to you, and that is CONGRATULATIONS, YOU ARE AMAZING. The method of calculation without calculus is complex, bordering on the ridiculous, but here it is:
Add together 39 x the square of the larger diameter, 25 times the square of the smaller diameter and 26 times the product of the two diameters. Multiply all that by the length, and divide by the magic number 26,489.84.

99. Bubbles in the Bath

The scientific explanation is not in doubt. In the shape of a sphere 1 cm^3 is contained by 4.835 cm^2 of surface area. In the shape of a cube 1 cm^3 is contained by 6 cm^2 of surface area.

100. Cannon Balls

The velocity of an 18 lb cannon ball fired with the same charge would be 923.37 ft per second.

101. The Playing Field

If little Billy Wiz ran at 5 m per second for 28.28 seconds he covered a distance of 141.4 m, this being the diagonal length of the field. The area of a square can be found by squaring the diagonal and dividing by two, so the area of the field is 9,997 m^2.

102. The Inscribed Circle

The area available to Nanny the goat is a circle inscribed in an isosceles triangle. The area of the circle is, of course Pi multiplied by the radius squared. The radius of the circle may be found by multiplying half the length of the base of the triangle with the tangent of half the base angle. In this case the area of the circular section of pasture is:
3.142(5 x Tan 35)(5 x Tan 35) = 38.5 m^2.

103. The Circumscribed Circle

The radius of the cutter is found by dividing half the distance between the vertices by the Cosine of half the angle between them. Twice this will give the diameter of the hole it will produce:
2(2.5/cos 30) = 2(2.5/0.8660) = 5.77 cm.

104. The Builder's Conundrum

The only possible way for three services

to be connected to three houses without crossing over each other is to introduce a third dimension. All three must follow exactly the same route one above the other. They can then enter the houses and separate in the directions required without ever crossing over one another.

105.   There's a Hole in my Bucket

The volume of the bucket (the technical name for this shape is a conical frustum) is best found by the use of this formula: add the square of larger radius to the square of the smaller radius and add to this the product of the two radii. Multiply this by Pi (3.142) and then by the height and divide the total by three. Thus: (15 x 15) + (10 x 10) + (15 x 10) x 3.142 x 25 divided by 3 = 12,435.5 This gives the answer in milliliters. At the rate of one ml per second, this number represents the number of seconds it will take for the bucket to empty. Changing this into hours, minutes and seconds we have the answer 3 hours 27 minutes and 15.5 seconds.

106.   Stop the Leak

You have been asked to find the volume of an elliptical ungulas of a conical frustum made by a section passing diagonally through opposite edges of the ends. First multiply the two diameters together and find the square root of the product. Multiply this by the larger diameter and subtract the square of the smaller diameter. Now divide all this by the difference between the two diameters. Multiply your answer first by the smaller diameter, then by the height of the bucket and then by Pi and divide all that by 12. Your answer will be in milliliters; divide by 1,000 to change it into liters: 4.383 liters.

107.   Going into Orbit

One-third of the earth's surface will be visible from a distance away from the earth that is exactly the same as the diameter of the earth, 7,914 miles.

108.   The Wicked Queen

Sam put his hand into the bag and drew out a pebble. Without looking at it, he let it fall to the pathway, where it was immediately lost. 'Butterfingers!' Sam said loudly. 'Never mind, we can tell which one I chose by looking at the color of the one left in the bag.' And they all lived happily ever after.

109.   The Pentagon

The length of the side of a pentagon is the same as the hypotenuse of a right-angled triangle whose height is the radius of the circle; the base is 5/8 the radius of the circle. The length can be found using Pythagoras' theorem simplified to the square root of 1.391 x 36 = 7.1 cm. This is the length of the side of a pentagon enclosed in a circle of 12 cm diameter.

110.   Squares and Circles

The smaller box, when fitted inside the globe, will touch the circumference with its corners. This means that the diagonal of the box is the diameter of the globe. When the globe is placed in the larger box it too touches the sides, which in turn means that the diameter of the globe is the same as the length of the sides of the larger box. The small box has a volume of 1 liter, which is 1,000 cm^3, so the length of the side of the small box is the cube root of 1,000 = 10. To find the volume of the larger box, take the length of the side of the smaller box, multiply it by the square root of three (this being the length of the side of the larger box) and cube it: $(10 \times 1.732)^3$ = 5,196.1524 cm^3 or 5.196 liters.

111.   The Wine Glass and the Crystal Ball

The best way to find the volume of the spilled wine is to find the volume of the part left above the level of the glass. Subtract this from the total volume of the crystal ball, and you will have the volume of the spillage. The volume of the sphere is 4/3 of the radius cubed, multiplied by Pi:

4/3 x 2 x 2 x 2 x 3.142 = 33.515
The volume of the section of the sphere above the glass is found by three times the diameter minus twice the height of the segment, times Pi, times the height squared and all of that divided by six. The height of the segment above the glass is 1.345 in (this can be proved by trigonometry):
[(3 x 4) - (2 x 1.35)] x 3.142 x (1.35 x 1.35) divided by 6 = 8.876
33.515 - 8.876 = 24.639 in^3 of spilled wine.

112. Wire It Up

The length of the wire may be found by dividing the cross-sectional area of the wire into the volume of the block of copper. The volume of 1 ft^3 of copper is 12 x 12 x 12 = 1,728 in^3.
The cross-sectional area of the wire is 3.142 x 0.0125 x 0.0125 = 0.00049087385 in^2.
1,728/0.00049087385 = 3,520,252.7 in.
Divide by 36 to change it into yards = 97,784.8.
Divide by 1,760 to change it into miles = 55.56 miles.

113.   Belt Up

The way to calculate the length of a belt between two pulleys of different sizes is found by first getting the surfaces in contact with the belt: $2\emptyset R_s$ and $2(\pi-\emptyset)R_l$, where R_s is the smaller and R_l the larger radii, and ø the angle (in radians) between radii tangent to the belt. To these add $2D_c\sin\emptyset$, the free belt lengths, where D_c is the center distance. The answer, once you've calculated everything out, is 151.73cm.

114.   Bridge over Troubled Water

The cost of building the bridge over the center of the pond would be $100 x 140 = $14,000. The length of the bridge at the new position is found by twice the square root of the width of the two sections of pond multiplied together. The pond would be split in a ratio of 3:1 which would give distances of 105 m and 35 m. The length of bridge at this point is twice the square root of 35 x 105 = 121.24 m. At $100 per meter this would incur a cost of $12,124 giving a saving of $1,876.

115.   The Legacy

This little problem is best solved by simple algebra. Let x = the amount of the increment. If number eight received $6,000, the shares received by the others will be as follows: the ninth will receive 6,000 - x, the tenth 6,000 - 2x, the seventh 6,000 + x, and the preceding ones 6,000 + 2x, 6,000 + 3x, 6,000 + 4x, 6,000 + 5x, 6,000 + 6x, 6,000 + 7x.
Adding all those together we have 60,000 + 25x. This must equal the total legacy of 100,000, so 60,000 + 25x = 100,000.
Then 25x = 40 000
x = 1600
So the ten grandchildren will receive, in order of preference: $17,200, $15,600, $14,000, $12,400, $10,800, $9,200, $7,600, $6,000, $4,400, $2,800.

116.   Fields of Corn

The two fields cover a total area of 30 acres. If we divide this by two we have the average size of the fields. Let X = the difference between the two areas. Then the first field yields (15 + X) x 40 kg of corn and the second (15 - X) x 30 kg of corn. The total difference between the amount the two fields produce is 500 kg:
40(15 + X) - 30(15 - X) = 500
600 + 40X - 450 + 30X = 500
150 + 70X = 500 so 70X = 350
And X = 5
So the areas of the fields are 15 + 5 = 20 acres and 15 - 5 = 10 acres.

117. The Three Wise Women

Let the three amounts that the ladies had in their purses be A, B and C, then we have:

A + B/2 + C/2 = 170 or 2A + B + C = 340 (i)

A/3 + B + C/3 = 170 or A + 3B + C = 510 (ii)

A/4 + B/4 + C = 170 or A + B + 4C = 680 (iii)

multiply (iii) by 2 and we have 2A + 2B + 8C = 1360 (iv)

(iv) minus (i) gives B + 7C = 1,020.
Dividing by 7 we have 130 remainder 110, so C = 130 and B = 110

Substituting into (iii): A + 110 + 4(130. = 680 we find A = 50

So the three amounts are $50, $110 and $130.

118. Fit for a King

The weights of the four metals to meet the king's specifications are:

Gold =	30.5 oz
Silver =	9.5 oz
Copper =	14.5 oz
Platinum =	5.5 oz
	60.0 oz

119. Tanks and Pipes

One way to solve this problem is to choose the size of the tank for yourself. Choose a number that will divide by 2, 3 and 4 – 12, say. Then in one day the first pipe delivers 12 gallons. The second pipe delivers 6 gallons in one day, the third 4 gallons and the smallest 3 gallons. Then in one day all four pipes will deliver 25 gallons when they are all running at once, but the tank that only holds 12 gallons so it will be full in 12/25 of one day.

12/25 x 24 hours = 11.52 hours
0.52 x 50 minutes = 31.2 minutes
So the tank will be full in 11 hours 31 minutes and 12 seconds.

120. The Charity Walk

Let x = the distance the first person has to walk and y = the measured amount, then the distances can be illustrated as:

x, x + y, x + 2y, x + 3y, x + 4y

Adding these together we have 5x + 10y = 100

So x + 2y = 20(i)

Also seven times the first two equal the last three, so 7(2x + y) = 3x + 9y, which becomes 14x +7y = 3x + 9y

So 11x = 2y   (ii)

Substituting in (i), 12x = 20, so x = 1.666˙ miles and y = 9.1666˙ miles.

The list would have been as follows:

First walker: 1.666˙ miles
Second walker: 10.833˙ miles
Third walker: 20.0 miles
Fourth walker: 29.16666˙ miles
Fifth walker: 38.333˙ miles

121. The Owl and the Weasel

Let x be the distance that both the owl and the weasel traveled before the point of interception and y be the distance from the hole. Then, using Pythagoras' theorem and letting the height of the tree equal one unit:

$x^2 = y^2 + 12$, but y = 3 - x
So $x^2 = (3 - x)(3 - x) + 1$
$x^2 = 9 - 6x - x^2 + 1$
0 = 10 - 6x
6x = 10
x = 1.6666'

So the distance of the point of interception is 3 - 1.666 = 1 1/3 times the height of the tree from the hole.

122. Unit Fractions

There are probably several different ways of solving this problem and possibly many different answers. I have chosen a method that avoids complicated progressions or formulae in order to make it easier to follow.

If we subtract a unit fraction which is as close to 2/103 as we can get from 2/103, then hopefully we should get an answer which is itself a unit fraction. 2/104 is very close to 2/103 and can be reduced to 1/52. Now if we subtract this from our original fraction we should find the second unit fraction.

$$\frac{2}{103} - \frac{1}{52}$$

$$\frac{104 - 103}{5,356} = \frac{1}{5,356}$$

So it follows that:

$$\frac{1}{52} + \frac{1}{5,356} = \frac{2}{103}$$

And to answer the conundrum x = 52, y = 5,356

123. The Six Brothers

Since the area of the triangle is 3,000 m^2, we can easily find the length of the base by dividing by the height and multiplying by two. The base is 50 m long and the height 120 m. If the height of the triangle is divided into six equal parts, each section must be 20 m wide.

Now each section decreases in area by the same increment, so it follows that the smallest area must be equal to that increment, since any further decrease by the same amount would result in zero area. The smallest area itself forms a triangle 1/6 the size of the larger, so its height must be 20 m and its base 50/6 = 8 1/3 m. Its area is therefore half of 20 x 8 1/3 = 83.333˙ m^2. This is the area of the increment.

124. In the Heat of the Sun

For the shadows to be equal in length to the height of the poles the sun must have been at an angle of 45° with the ground. There were no shadows at all when the truck broke down, so the sun would have then been at 90°. The earth rotates at a rate of 1° every four minutes, so 4 x 45 = 180 minutes. Thus help arrived at 3 p.m.

125. Busy Bees

The spiral is created by the circumference of five quarter circles, each one smaller than the last by the radius decreasing in

length equal to the size of side of the hive. The centers of each quarter circle are the corners of the hive, starting at the one before the entrance, working anti-clockwise around the hive and finishing back at the same point, so the length of the spiral flight of the bee is found by:

$$\frac{2 \times 3.142(2.5 + 2 + 1.5 + 1 + 0.5)}{4}$$

= 1/2 x 3.142 x 7.5 = 11.78 m.
The technical term for this type of spiral is the involute of the square.

126. A Roll of Ribbon

The ribbon is wound around a center core 1 cm in diameter, which has a circumference of 3.142 x 1. The roll is made up of ever increasing circles up to an overall diameter of 3 cm, so there is a 1 cm thickness of ribbon between the core and the outside edge. The ribbon is 0.01 cm thick, so there must be 100 windings in total, each one increasing in circumference by a constant amount. The overall circumference of the roll is 3.142 x 3 = 9.426 cm.

The length of ribbon for each winding must increase in length by the circumference of the roll minus the circumference of the inner core divided by 100.
(9.426 - 3.142)/100 = 0.06284.
To calculate the overall length of ribbon it is easier if we let x = 3.142 and y = 0.06284.
Overall length of ribbon:
= (x + y) + (x + 2y) + (x + 3y) + . . . + (x + 100y)
= 100x + 5,050y
= 314.2 + 317.34
= 631.54 cm or 6.3154 m.

127. A Pack of Candles

The radius of the inscribed circle of the hexagon is 1.37 times the diameter of the candles. A hexagon is made up of six equilateral triangles, each of which can be divided into two right-angled triangles. Now the radius of the inscribed circle is

the height of the triangle, and the base is half the hypotenuse. Since the side of the hexagon is equal to the hypotenuse, we can find this by Pythagoras' theorem.
Let x = the hypotenuse, then:
$x^2 - x^2/4 = 22.992$
$3x^2 = 91.968$
$x^2 = 30.656$
$x = 5.54$ cm, this being the required length.

128. To Catch the Train

Let x = distance from home to garage and y = distance from garage to station, then $x + y$ = distance from home to station.
Time = distance/speed
So $x/8 + y/40 = 21/60$
$40x + 8y = 112$
$5x + y = 14$ (i)
Also $x/16 + y/60 = 11\,1/2/60$
$60x + 16y = 184$
$15x + 4y = 46$ (ii)
(i) x 3 gives $15x + 3y = 42$ (iii)
(i) minus (iii) gives $y = 4$
Substitute in (i): $5x + 4 = 14$
So $x = 2$
Distance to station = $x + y$, so the distance is 6 km.

129. The Travelers

The number of people who took part in the survey was equal to or greater than 137.

130. The Pine Tree

The right triangle formed by the broken tree has a base of 5m and an altitude (a) and hypotenuse (h) which together are 25m. Hence, by Pythgaoras, $h^2 - a^2 = 5^2$, where $h+a = 25$. Solving the equations gives an altitude of 12m, the height at which lightning struck.

131. Sinking a Well

Letting A and B be the two constants for the two known wells, we can form two equations.

For the 10 m depth $100A + 1000B = 60$ (i)
And for the 150 m depth $225A + 3375B = 146.25$ (ii)

Multiplying (i) by 2.25 gives $225A + 2250B = 135$ (iii)
Subtract (iii) from (ii) and we have $1125B = 11.25$ so $B = 0.01$
Substituting in (i): $100A + 10 = 60$
$100A = 50$
$A = 0.5$
So we have the constants $A = 0.5$, $B = 0.01$. Using these we can find the cost of the 20 m well.
$202 \times 0.5 + 203 \times 0.01$ = time taken.
$200 + 80 = 280$ hours
280 hours at $50 per hour = $14,000

132. Find the Fraction

Let x = the numerator and y = the denominator, then:
$$\frac{x+y}{y+7} = \frac{5}{6} \qquad \text{and} \qquad \frac{x+5}{y+7} = \frac{3}{4}$$

Cross multiplication gives $6x + 42 = 5y + 35$ and $4x + 20 = 3y + 21$
Rearranging gives:
$5y - 6x = 7$ (i)
$3y - 4x = -1$ (ii)
(i) multiplied by 2 and (ii) multiplied by 3 gives:
$10y - 12x = 14$
$9y - 12x = -3$
Subtraction leads to $y = 17$
Substitute in (i):
$51 - 4x = -1$
$-4x = -52$
$x = 13$
So the original fraction is 13/17.

133. The Bowling Green

To raise the green by 1 ft in height, 60,000 ft^3 (200 x 300 x 1) of soil are needed. The trench would be 1,032 ft in length, 8 ft wide, and 7.27 ft deep.

134. An Old Babylonian Conundrum

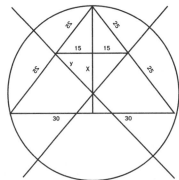

By using Pythagoras' theorem and similar triangles we can find the measurements shown in the diagram above. The radius of the circle is the distance from the intersection of the bisectors of the two sides to the vertices. If we can find a value for x and add it to 20 we have found the radius.
Now $(20 + x)^2 = 25^2 + y^2$, but $y^2 = 15^2 + x^2$

so $(20 + x)^2 = 25^2 + 15^2 + x^2$
$400 + 40x + x^2 = 625 + 225 + x^2$
$400 + 40x = 850$
$40x = 450$
$x = 11.25$
$11.25 + 20 = 31.25$. This is the radius of the circle.

135. De Morgan's Conundrum

The great Augustus De Morgan was 43 years old in the year 1849. He was born in 1806 and died in 1871 at the age of 65.

136. A Square in a Triangle

We can find the length of the side of the lawn if we find the area of the large triangle and subtract it from the areas of the three flower beds. This will leave us with the area of the lawn, and hence we can find the length required. We can find the height of the large triangle by using Pythagoras Theorem. This is 8 m. Calling the length of the side of the lawn x, the area of the upper triangle is 1/2 x(8 - x). Calling the length of the base of the two lower triangles y, then their areas are 2(1/2xy), but from the base of the large triangle we can see that x + 2y = 12, so y = 6 - x/2.
So the area of the lower triangles = 2(1.2 x (6 - x/2)), which equals x (6 - x/2).
Now the area of the lawn is x, so the area of the large triangle is x + x(6 - x/2) + 1/2x (8 - x) = 48
Removing brackets gives:
x + 6x - x/2 + 4x - x/2 = 48
Collecting terms:
10x = 48
so x = 4.8
The length of the side of the lawn is 4.8 m.

137. Buried Treasure

To answer the cabin boy's question we must add together all the fractions plus 10 plus 1. If we let x = the number of coins found, then:
x/3 + x/4 + x/5 + x/8 + 10 + 1 = x
LCD = 120, so we have 40x/120 + 30x/120 + 24x/120 + 15x/120 = x - 11
Which gives:
109x = 120x - 1320
11x = 1320
x = 120
So the pirates found 120 gold coins.

138. The Farmer's Fields

This problem can be solved by using quadratic equations, but to save you the trouble, the dimensions of the two fields are 30 m^2 and 10 m^2.

139. Sharing the Winnings

For $180 to be divided into six parts in such a way as to give a constant difference between the amounts and the sum of the four larger shares to be $5^3/_7$ times the sum of the two smaller shares, the sums have to be:

$10, $18, $26, $34, $42 and $50 exactly. This gives a difference between the sums of $8, and $5^3/_7(10 + 18) = (26 + 34 + 42 + 50) = 152.

140. Washing the Blanket

Poor Mrs D. Tergent's blanket is now only 78.75 per cent of its original size, so it has shrunk by 21.25 per cent.

141. Stacking the Shelves

The new shelf would hold 60 packets of cereal. In the ratio of 1:2:3:4 the display would hold six packets of type A, 12 of type B, 18 of type C and 24 of type D.

142. The Three Drunks

Those three foolish men drank a total of 15 liters of beer, which means that they drank 26 imperial pints (32 US pints) between them. Stan drank four more than Bill, and Fred drank four more than Stan. If we let x = the number that Bill drank then:

$x + (x + 4) + (x + 8) = 32$
$3x + 12 = 32$
$3x = 20$
$x = 6 2/3$

So Bill drank 5 imperial pints (6 2/3 US pints), Stan drank 9 imperial pints (10 2/3 US pints) and Fred drank 12 imperial pints (14 2/3 US pints).

143. A Cubic Calendar

The numbers on the first cube are 0, 1, 2, 3, 4 and 5, and the numbers on the second cube are 0, 1, 2, 6, 7 and 8. 'But what about number nine?' I can almost hear you cry.

'Turn the six upside down,' is my reply.

144. A Five-Letter Word

A five-letter word containing two vowels and three consonants, all of which are alike, is the word ERROR. There may be more than one answer to this conundrum, so if you have thought of a different word, well done.

145. An Angle in Time

If we take 12 o'clock to be zero°, then for every hour the small hand moves 30°, and for every minute the large hand moves 6°. If it is a quarter past the hour the large hand has moved 90°. For the angle between the two to be 37.5° the hour hand has to have moved either 90 - 37.5° or 90 + 37.5°, that is 52.5° or 127.5°. 52.5° of movement would show a time movement of 1 3/4 hours, making it 1.45. This cannot be correct, as the large hand shows a quarter past the hour, not a quarter to. 127.5° would show a time movement of 4 1/4 hours. So the time is now 4.15. In 20 minutes time the hour will move another 10° and the minute hand another 120°, giving angles of 137.5° and 210° respectively, a difference of 72.5°.

146. From an Ellipse to a Circle

An elliptical cylinder whose major axis is twice its minor axis cut by an inclined plane will form a perfect circle when the cut is made at 60° to the horizontal along the major axis.

147. The More You Buy, the More You Get

The flower seller offered flowers at 10 for $4 to begin with. He then added another seven flowers and increased the price by $1. He then added another nine flowers and $1 to the price. He finally added another 11 flowers and a further $1 to the price, so he was offering 26 flowers for $6.

148. Changing the Patio

The patio measured 26 ft by 22 ft and was made from square flagstones, each one measuring 2 ft x 2 ft. This means there were 143 flagstones in the construction. Anyone attempting to solve this puzzle by making a scale drawing of Mr Mason's patio will probably count that 22 flagstones have to be cut. If the drawing were life-size, they would find that, in reality, 23 would fall under the saw's path, leaving 120 untouched. The diagonal cut divides the patio into two triangles of equal area, so 60 uncut flagstones would be recovered.

149.   Cowboy Joe

If Cowboy Joe heads straight to the river at a point 2.5 miles downstream he will cover a distance of 5.59 miles. After watering his horse, if he travels directly to his cabin he will cover a distance of 7.826 miles, a total distance of 13.416 miles. This is his shortest possible route.

150.   The Pool Player

The way out is to imagine a mirror is placed against the cushion opposite the red ball. The player should now aim the white ball directly at the reflection of the red. If you make a point on the diagram that represents the position of the reflection of the red ball and draw a straight line from this point to the white ball, you will find the point of contact with the cushion is at position three.

151.   The Case of the Different Areas

On one side of the diagonal line we have an area of 71 cm^2 and on the other 72 cm^2, yet if we ignore the sub-divisions we find that both sides of the diagonal have equal areas of 71.5 cm^2. Obviously something is wrong. Looking at the two triangular sub-divisions we find that the angle the hypotenuse makes with the base is different in each case. A five by six triangle forms a base angle of 39.8°, so the diagonal is not a straight line. This is what is wrong with the diagram.

152.   The Dripping Tap

Most people who attempted to solve this puzzle will have calculated the number of minutes between 3.36 and 7.00, multiplied the answer by 60 to find the number of seconds, and divided by 17. They will

have found the answer to be 720. Sorry, this is not the right answer. The first drip occurred exactly as I started counting. Yes, there were 720 intervals of 17 seconds each, but I counted 721 drips.

153.   The Edges of a Polyhedron

The mathematician Euler made an interesting discovery about the relationship between the number of faces, vertices and edges of polyhedra. If you add the number of faces and the number of vertices together and subtract the number of edges, you always arrive at the answer two. This is true for all the five different possible types of polyhedra. If we let F = faces, V = vertices and E = edges, then:

F + V - E = 2

In this case F = 20 and V = 12, so:

20 + 12 - E = 2

The icosahedron must have 30 edges.

154.   The Kingdom of Truth

The wife replied, 'I will be burned alive.' The king then handed the responsibility of carrying out the sentence over to the court. Her reply caused such confusion and debate among the learned judges that the case was dropped, just as the king had planned.

155.   Missing Number

The number I am thinking of is -1.

156.   How Old is Grandma?

Grandma is 59 years young.

157.   Come into My Parlor

Simultaneous equations, with x=number of flies (which have six legs) and y=number of spiders (which have eight legs), are 6x + 8y = 166, and x + y = 25. Therefore the solution is that there are 17 flies and 8 spiders.

158.   The Cowboy Plumber

The expansion of metal is calculated by multiplying the length of the pipe by the increase in temperature and the co-efficient of expansion. This gives:

Length = 120 ft x 12 = 1440 in

Increase in temperature = 145

Co-efficient of expansion of steel = 0.000012

1440 x 145 x 0.000012 = 2.5056.

The pipe would increase in length by over 2.5 in.

159.   The Speed Boat

The original speed of the boat was 12 km per hour.

160.   Changing the Fraction

If the fraction 3/5 is written as 15/25 it can easily be seen that the number added to both the numerator and the denominator of 7/17 is 8.

161.   Consecutive Numbers

The two consecutive numbers that have a difference of 53 between their squares are 26 and 27. The difference between the squares of two consecutive integers is always one more than twice the lower number or one less than twice the higher number.

162.   Bingo

The probability that neither Alan nor Gary will cross off a number on the first draw is 11/15.

The probability that Alan crosses a number off on both the first and second draws is 2/87.

The probability of only Alan crossing off a number and then only Gary crossing off a number is 3/290.

163.   The Cost of a Call

Before the increase 30 seconds were allowed for 1 cent.

164.   The Seating Arrangement

The most profitable seating arrangement is to have 40 easy chairs (four rows of 10) and 72 upright chairs (six rows of 12). Total box office sales = $412.

165.   From the Mouths of Babes

As water cools it becomes heavier and sinks to the bottom of the pond. When it reaches a temperature of 4°C it is at its heaviest. As the temperature drops below this, the water starts to become lighter and slowly rises to the surface. When it reaches a temperature of zero° it is lighter than the water on the bottom of the pond, and it freezes on the surface.

166.   Pythagoras Revisited

Yes. The area of any shape on the hypotenuse of a right-angled triangle is equal to the sum of the areas of similarly proportioned shapes, such as circles or equilateral triangles, drawn on the other sides.

167.   A Game of Marbles

The numbers of marbles the boys had at the end of the game are 6, 18, 19, 20, 21 and 36, so the boy who lost the most had only six marbles left at the end of the game.

168.   A Tale of Two Ladders

The two ladders cross each other at a distance 10.45 ft above the ground.

169.   The Three-Number Problem

The three numbers are 6, 12 and 36.

170.   The Genius of Hipparchus

The method here may be a slight simplification, but it contains the essence of Hipparchus' method of calculating the distance from the earth to the moon. Let us suppose that the calculation was made at a time when a line from the center of the earth to the center of the moon cuts the surface of the earth at a point on the equator. We can then imagine another line from the center of the moon to the earth's surface that forms a tangent to the earth and just touches the surface. The radius of the earth will meet the tangent at 90°, and the three lines form a right-angled triangle. The angle made between the radius of the earth and the line joining the centers of the two bodies is the latitude of the point where the tangent touches the earth's surface. A reasonable value for this latitude is 89.05°, and the radius of the earth is about 3,950 miles. Hence the distance between the center of the earth and the center of the moon is found by 3,950 divided by Cosine 89.05.

Distance = 3,950/0.01658 = 238,000 miles.

171. We Are Sailing

In order to solve this conundrum we need to choose a distance for the voyage. Choose a distance which is divisible by two, three and four – say 12. With the largest sail only in use, the ship travels at a speed of six miles per day. The next largest will drive the ship at a speed of four miles per day, and the smallest three miles per day. With all three sails in use together the ship should make a speed of 13 miles per day. Divide by 24 to find miles per hour, and we have 0.54166˙ mph. At a speed of 0.54166˙ mph we should cover a distance of 12 miles in 12/0.54166 hours = 22.154 hours or 22 hours nine minutes. This will be true whatever the actual distance of the voyage happens to be.

172. Reducing the Cube

The width of the cube is reduced by 2/3. That means it is 1/3 of its original width. The length of the cube is trebled, so the product of the length and the width is the same for the cuboid as it was for the cube. This leaves us with the height only to consider. The height is reduced by one half; this will reduce the volume by half. The volume of the cuboid is 864 cm^3, so the original volume of the cube must have been 1,728 cm^3.

If we now find the cube root of 1,728 we will have the length of the side of the cube: 12 cm.

173. Disks in a Rectangle

The radius of the second disk is 1.254 cm.

174. Plane for Hire

The original number of people in the party was 30, and the final price each of the remaining passengers had to pay was $45.

175. In the Foundry

In order to find the radius of the original cylinder we must first find the volume. This will be the same as the volume of the hexagon rod. To find this volume we multiply the area of the end of the rod by its length. The end of a hexagon rod is made up of six equilateral triangles, each with sides of length 2 cm. The area of each of these triangles is half the base times the height. The height of each triangle can be found by Pythagoras' theorem and is the square root of three, i.e.. 1.732, so the volume of the rod and hence the cylinder is 1.732 x 1 x 6 x 25 = 10.392.

The radius of the original cylinder is found by dividing this number by the length of the cylinder and by Pi and then finding the square root the answer = 3.437 or 3.5 cm.

The volume of the contents of the tank is found by the radius x radius x Pi x the length of the hexagon rod: 5 x 5 x 3.142 x 25 = 1,963.6 cm^3.

Subtract the volume of the hexagon rod and divide the answer by the radius x radius x Pi:

1,963.5 - 259.8/5 x 5 x 3.142 = 21.7 cm. This is the depth of fluid before the rod is inserted.

176. The Hikers

There are two ways to solve this and the next two conundrums. One is to draw a scale diagram and measure the distances asked for. The other is by calculation using the Cosine rule. For those people who do not wish to do either, the answer is: Jones and Brown would have to each walk a distance of 1.55 miles to reach Smith.

After Brown has walked back the way he came for half an hour, Jones would have to walk a distance of 2.6 miles to reach him.

Smith would have to walk 1.867 miles to where Brown is waiting.

177.   Working with Sheet Metal
There are several ways to work out the dimensions of the width of the 'T' piece, one of which involves quadratic equations. To save you the trouble, the answer is 2.3435 cm.

178.   In the Hotel Dining Room
The center of the plane face of the hemisphere lies in the center of the bottom face of the block of cheese. The upper corners of the cheese all lie on the inside surface of the hemisphere, so the distance from the center of the bottom face of the cheese to any of the top corners is the radius of the hemisphere. We use Pythagoras to find the center of the bottom surface, i.e. the square root of $3 \times 3 + 2 \times 2 = 3.6$ in.
Now we use Pythagoras again to find the radius: the square root of $3.6 \times 3.6 + 3 \times 3 = 4.69$ in.
This is the radius of the hemisphere.

179.   From Town to Town
Let the car meet the walkers after T hours. So the walkers are then 4T miles form the first town. The car covered the journey between the two towns in 1 1/3 hours, so it meets the walkers in a further (T - 1 1/3) hours; therefore it meets the walkers 30(T - 1 1/3) miles from the next town. However, the two towns are 40 miles apart, so:
$4T + 30(T - 1 1/3) = 40$
$34T = 80$

$T = 40/17$
After picking up the walkers, the car has to cover the distance 30(T - 1 1/3) miles = 30 x 40/17 - 3/4 miles = 520/17 miles in order to get back to the next town. This journey will take 520/17 divided by 30 hours = 52/51 hours. So the total time taken for the party to complete their journey is 40/17 + 52/51 = 172/51 hours. The party arrives at the next town just after 3.22 p.m.

180.   The Tetrahedron
The volume of a tetrahedron is found by the formula: 1/3 x base area x height. Since one of the triangles will form the base we already know the base area = Root 3. To find the height of the tetrahedron we can use Pythagoras. Forming a right-angled triangle, the hypotenuse of which is the height of one of the equilateral triangles, gives us root 3. The base of the right-angled triangle will be the distance from the center of one of the sides to a point directly under the apex of the tetrahedron. This point will be exactly 1/3 of the height of the equilateral triangles, 1/3 root 3, so the volume of the tetrahedron is:
1/3 of the square root of (root 32 minus one third of root 32) multiplied by root three. All this equals 0.9428 centimeters[3].

181.   The Sum of the Fractions
The number is 120.

182.   Percentage Increase
The cost price of producing the goods is 60 cents per kilo.

183.   A Six-Shaded Problem
Assigning numbers to letters (A = 1, B = 2, C = 3, etc.), yellow plus brown will equal 164.

184.   The Fun Run
Let Alan = A, Bill = B and Charlie = C, then A + B + C = 21.
But A = 5B and C = 2A - 3; therefore C =